Caballus Publishers

BOX 2307 FORT COLLINS, COLORADO 80521

THE HORSE BOOK PEOPLE

CARE AND BREEDING OF HORSES

edited and revised by
WILLIAM E. JONES
D.V.M. , Ph.D
From Material on *The Horse*

No. 7 IN THE HORSE HEALTH AND CARE SERIES

ISBN   0-912830-08-5

Library of Congress Catalog Card No.

73-85946

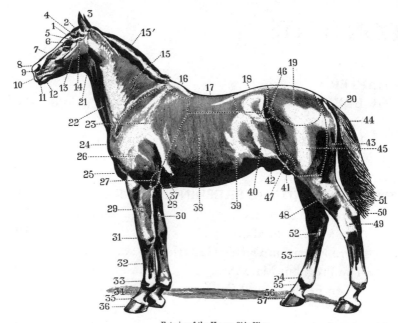

Exterior of the Horse: Side View

REFERENCES

1 Forehead.	19 Croup.	39 Abdomen.
2 Forelock.	20 Tail.	40 Flank.
3 Ear.	21 Throat.	41 Testicles.
4 Supra-orbit.	22 Cervical Groove.	42 Sheath.
5 Eyebrow.	23 Shoulder.	43 Buttock.
6 Eye.	24 Shoulder Point.	44 Point of Buttock.
7 Nose.	25 Breast.	45 Thigh.
8 Nasal Peak.	26 Upper Arm.	46 Haunch.
9 Nostril.	27 Elbow.	47 Stifle.
10 Upper Lip.	28 Point of Elbow.	48 Leg or Gaskin.
11 Lower Lip.	29 Forearm.	49 Hock.
12 Chin.	30 Chestnut.	50 Point of Hock.
13 Cheek.	31 Knee.	51 Tendo Achilles or Ham-string.
14 Temple.	32 Canon.	52 Chestnut.
15 Neck.	33 Fetlock-joint.	53 Canon.
15' Crest.	34 Pastern.	54 Fetlock-joint.
16 Withers.	35 Coronet.	55 Pastern.
17 Back.	36 Foot.	56 Coronet.
18 Loins.	37 Brisket.	57 Foot.
	38 Chest.	

CONTENTS

PREFACE

A new breed of professional horsebreeders has created a demand today for good detailed information about the management and raising of horses. Although our libraries are chocked with general books for the novice on horse care, there is a dearth of solid factual information available on the care and breeding of horses.

This material was compiled in an effort to fill the void. Much of the practical advice offered here is taken from "tried and true" experience accumulated and recorded during the peak of horse breeding activities at the turn of the century in England, the cradle of modern horse breeding as we know it today. With this as a foundation on which to build, details of modern techniques and new knowledge have been added, resulting in what I hope will be a helpful book for anyone wanting to become better informed and more successful in his horsebreeding venture.

William E. Jones
Fort Collins, Colorado
1974

Nothing more satisfying

I. THE BREEDING FARM

There is nothing more satisfying in the horse business than the breeding of an outstanding horse. To win a race over a course, or a prize in a show ring, affords a certain amount of pleasure, and maybe some profit. While allowing that to bring a horse into a condition to accomplish either of these feats entails a certain amount of intelligence and skill, it falls far short of yielding that gratification which is afforded by having overcome the far more difficult task of producing the animal.

To breed a winner of a classic race or a champion of the first class is unquestionably the goal. Although success in these respects seldom comes, even to the most patient and painstaking. But this should be rather an encouragement than a deterrent, for the more difficult the task the greater the honor.

We could point to many men who, with control of large studs, have spent a lifetime in honest endeavor to realize these higher ambitions without attaining success; but they have done the next best thing, producing stock of a high standard of excellence. After all, that is what the general breeder desires and what the country requires--a grading up as near to the highest attainable point as can be reached.

In breeding operations a certain percentage of the produce of the stud are sure to fall below mediocrity in conformation and character, and others, for various reasons, will fail to prove profitable. To guard against these adverse influences is the great problem which the breeder should strive to solve, and upon which his highest success will depend.

The general quality of horses has improved tremendously over the last few decades. If a breeder now expects to make additional improvements he will be forced to follow rather rigidly the established principles of good breeding.

1

Even the non-purebred horses of today have attained a rather high degree of excellence in comparison to thirty or forty years ago. In days gone by the grade horse could usually be identified by his ill-make and shape. He was a leggy, cow-hocked, narrow-gutted, light chested, heavy crested brute, with a back that made the most daring fear to put anything on it; besides which his disposition and endurance were of the worst.

The goals of the typical professional horsebreeder have been refined tremendously. Rather than having to concentrate most of his effort on breeding for soundness, he can now devote his selection pressure towards the attainment of breed specific individuals. In fact today, if horse breeding is to be financially successful, the breeder must know and be consciously working towards the production of horses that fit the ideal for his breed.

FACILITIES

Conditions conducive to health are of the first importance to success in the breeding and rearing of horses, and however well designed the plans may be in other respects, neglect of this cardinal point is sure to end in failure.

The man who is willing to invest his money in the purchase of good stock at the outset, should be sure that nothing stands in the way of maintaining and enhancing its high standard of excellence. For the lack of this precaution the writer has witnessed many painful examples of failure and disappointment.

A good site constitues the bed-rock on which the foundation of a profitable breeding farm should be laid. A high and dry position, sheltered from the west and north by rising ground, is the most desirable site, and where choice is permissible should be selected.

It is not, however, to be understood that a less elevated position is necessarily objectionable. This would depend a good deal on the nature and porosity of the soil, the extent and efficiency of drainage, and whether the country was heavily wooded or open. While the bluegrass country of Kentucky is generally concepualized as the ideal type of environment for raising horses, it is not entirely necessary. Soil suitable for breeding and rearing horses, although variable in its nature, is influenced in a great measure by the extent to which it is drained and wooded. In a well-drained, open country, where the moisture is carried off and not allowed to stagnate and become dissipated merely by evaporation, a fairly strong clay may prove useful; while the converse of these conditions will render the air so humid and damp, and the soil so cold, that both plant and animal life will be prejudicially affected. Trees and fences, by breaking the force of the wind and affording shelter from storms, are most desirable adjuncts in due proportion and when suitably disposed, but when existing in excess they not only impart dampness to the district by preventing the free circulation of air, but in summer-time they form a breeding-ground for flies, which worry and torment horses so that grazing is interfered with and constant stamping provoked, causing serious damage to legs, and especially to those of growing animals.

To go into the subject of geological formation best suited to the breeding of horses would open up a very difficult and debatable question. To what extent it influences the success or failure of breeding operations it is impossible to say. Good horses are raised in almost every part of the country. One important consideration, however, has to do with the mineral content of the soil and subsequently the feed that grows thereon. Proper amounts of calcium and phosphorus are essential as well as adequate amounts of a dozen or so trace elements. Feed supplements in common use today can generally alleviate any problem that might arise from lack of minerals. Therefore even this consideration becomes negligible.

The physical conformation of a country is important. Hill land is usually dry and is conducive to good health, but, generally speaking, lacks fertility, and is not so sustaining as that in less elevated positions. It offers, however, advantages which are of considerable importance to the growing animal. The pasterns acquire slope, elasticity is imparted to the paces, and action is developed. The feet, too, acquire strength, with ample size and good formation. It is often claimed that rocky soils have the advantage of keeping hooves in better shape and in developing sure-footedness.

Nothing is more important to the well-being of the

breeding farm than a supply of wholesome water. Where ponds, rivers, wells, and streams are the sources it will be necessary to investigate them as to how they are fed or replenished, and in what relation they stand to possible sources of contamination with matters prejudicial to health.

Rivers on whose banks manufacturing industries are carried on, are liable to be polluted with various deleterious waste products of manufacture, and the danger to animal health will in such cases be in proportion as the stream is slow and small in volume, or rapid and large. In times of drought, when water is low and sedimentary matters come to the surface and are stirred up by the feet of horses while drinking, the danger is materially augmented, not only as regards chemical substances and decomposing organic matter, but also in reference to parasitic infection.

Ponds should be periodically cleansed. No trees should be allowed to overhang them, and to obtain the greatest security against mischief they should be fenced off and the water lifted into tanks placed beside them. This is especially desirable during periods of drought, when they are low, and the decomposing sediment teeming with animal and vegetable life is brought near to the surface.

Purity is not a possible condition in nature, and cannot therefore be hoped for, but as far as practicable an ample and wholesome supply should at all times be accessible to breeding-stock and their produce. Neglect of this precaution may be responsible for some outbreaks of abortion and infertility which so frequently occur in our large breeding-studs, and it should ever be present to the mind of the breeder that however wholesome water may be at its source and in its course, dangerous pollution may nevertheless result where tanks and troughs are allowed to be fouled by animal and vegetable matters. The periodical cleansing of these receptacles, therefore, is indispensable to good management and success in breeding operations.

The buildings required vary in as great a multitude as geographical locations and climatic conditions. It is generally most practicable to house the stallion in a private paddock with his own barn or shed. Large spacious stalls should be provided for foaling, generally several being located in a single barn.

Small breeding establishments can often provide individual stalls and paddocks for each animal the year around, but this is certainly not a necessity. On the larger farms horses are grouped together in catagories such as mares in foal, mares with foal, yearlings, dry mares, etc. Whether these groups of animals are in a pasture or a large dry lot, the housing is often no more than a large shed entirely open along one side.

Stocking and overstocking are clearly relative terms. The number of animals a definite area of land will carry will of course depend upon the fertility of the soil and its power of sustaining growth through the year, as well as upon the nature and character of the herbage it produces. Horses have a strong predilection for the finer grasses, and from a grazing point of view may be regarded as wasteful feeders. Nothing is more striking than the way in which they will clear the grass off certain patches down to the roots, and continue to graze the ground over again and again, while other parts of the pasture are covered with a luxuriant growth which they altogether neglect. Acreage, therefore, is no absolute mea-

A large shed entirely open along one side.

sure of the sustaining power of pasture land, but rather the quantity and quality of suitable herbage it produces. Among other reasons, it is this partiality to certain parts of pastures which has rendered it desirable to provide a large area of ground for horses to run over.

Nothing tends so much to the deterioration of pasture land as overstocking with horses. By this is not to be understood the mere placing on it of more horses than it can fairly support, but grazing it year after year without fertilizing and pasture rotation. Pasture rest, fertilization and rotation prevents it from becoming boggy and foul, serving as a suitable environment for the growth and maturation of the larvae of equine parasites, which, when once introduced, continue to multiply year by year, invading first one animal and then another, until under favorable conditions the great bulk of the breeding-stock become more or less severely infected. Poverty, stunted growth, infertility, and abortion are among the consequences of this too common mismanagement. Land devoted to horsebreeding should be periodically grazed with cattle or mown for hay.

FOUNDATION STOCK

No man should undertake the breeding of horses who has not first acquainted himself with the principle of genetics and inheritance. For it is only then can he realize how difficult it is to obtain a uniform result from what appears to be the same set of circumstances. He may rely on each variety being true to itself--that quarter horses will produce quarter horses; hackneys, hackneys; thoroughbreds, thoroughbreds, & etc.; but he cannot rely on one or another to reproduce offspring of a uniform standard of excellence. Moreover, the same dam and the same sire mated through a succession of years will frequently be found to yield produce essentially dissimilar from each other in form, color, endurance, and temperament. On this account breeding has been said to be a 'lottery', and in many respects cannot be better expressed. Influenced in a large measure by causes which are beyond our control, and which we but vaguely comprehend, the element of chance must necessarily enter largely into the enterprise. But on the other hand, there is ample experience to show that the uncertainty incidental

Foundation stock

to horse-breeding may be greatly curtailed by the adoption of proper methods.

The natural tendency of both animals and plants in the course of propagation is to vary either in one or more of their parts, or as a whole, and this will be more especially the case in those specimens which have been rapidly forced to a higher state of development by artificial selection and treatment.

Beyond this there also exists a tendency, in these improved forms especially, to revert or throw back to a more or less remote ancestor, and in doing so the offspring may depart from the parental type by losing the more recently acquired and much-coveted characters. It is on this account that inbreeding so forcibly calls for careful scrutiny and consideration in stud-management.

With these facts in view, it is not difficult to understand why produce so frequently differ from each other, and from the parents from which they spring, and why the fundamental belief that 'like produces like' is so frequently untrue. Many a breeder has experienced the disappointment of producing an unshapely, worthless brute from an alliance of his choicest stock.

Derby-winners and the commonest of scrubs have frequently descended from the same parents. Champions and cup-winners claim family kinship with plugs and skates as the result of these genetic variables.

Of course, discrepancies of this kind are not always referrable to the causes alleged. Some are brought about by accident or neglect, in which sickness and indifferent feeding and housing play an important part; but the natural tendency to variation, and to revert to ancestors less improved or of inferior type, is accountable for much of the diversity of size, form, color, temperament, and endurance so frequently encountered in the experience of horse-breeders.

To minimize the risks which must always attend the breeding of horses, and especially the improved breeds, it should be the aim and object of whoever enters upon the business to procure at the outset some of the best specimens of the variety he wishes to reproduce.

Outward form, however, is not necessarily the passport to success, but with that must be combined the property of prepotency, or power on the part of the breeding-stock to impress their meritorious points, size, form, action, power, quality, & etc. upon their offspring. This property, largely possessed by certain strains or families, is but feebly exercised by others.

It is equally important that this power to impart to the offspring the best qualities of the parent should be as strongly implanted in the dam as it is in the sire, and it should also have existed in the ancestors of both for a succession of generations.

This means that individual merit alone cannot be relied upon to perpetuate itself, unless fixed in the individual by a long succession of prepotent ancestors.

How often do we see in our show-rings horses and mares possessing the most perfect form and action, whose offspring never rise beyond mediocrity, and for the most part hardly reach that. Such animals are usually examples of extreme variation or reversion, whose high standard of excellence ends with the individual instead of being perpetuated in the race by the force of heredity.

How often do we see in our showrings horses and mares possessing the most perfect form and action, whose offspring never rise above mediocracy?

Good characters to be transmitted to the offspring with reasonable regularity must be strongly inherited by the parents from remote ancestors. There must be a deep-rooted faculty in the family for reproducing their best traits of character.

Animals so constituted, when mated together yield the best results, and by a process of selection the breeder is enabled to grade his stock upward, and thus improve the race.

It must, however, be remembered that this power to reproduce all that is best in conformation and constitution may be equally effective in transmitting any faults which may appear in the one or the other.

Where a weak point is found to exist in the make-up of a breeding animal, care should be taken to mate it with one which is not only strong in that particular respect, but decended from parents in whom the required quality was also a conspicuous feature. Only those who realize the importance of inbreeding and its influence in shaping the offspring can hope to make breeding a profitable enterprise.

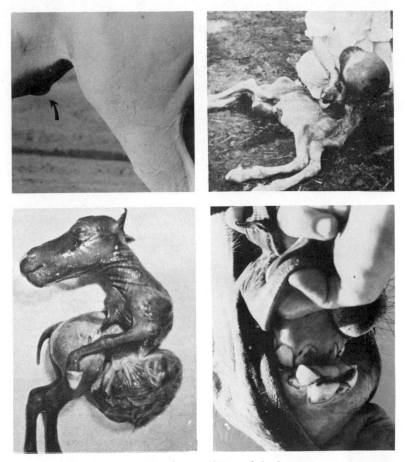

Some genetic abnormalities of the horse

II. THE MARE AND
THE BREEDING PROGRAM

At what age mares should be put to the stud has always been a question around which much controversy has gathered among breeders of horses; but whatever differences may exist in the matter of opinion, there can be no doubt as to the very general practice in vogue, which allows them to commence their stud career at two years old. This system of early mating is more prevalent among breeders of pedigree stock than among those who engage more especially in the production of grade horses. The latter recognize the physiological truth, that the highest development is reached where the nutritive resources of the system are devoted exclusively to its own maintenance, and not shared by the growing fetus, the main object being to encourage growth and development, and produce a horse with size, substance, and constitution.

Pedigree, and the glamour of family fame which attaches to it, too frequently prompts the indiscretion of breeding from babies, and the demand for special produce may, from a commercial point of view, justify such a course; but no one with any knowledge of the laws of life can doubt that to impose upon a mare the task of reproduction while actively engaged in building up her own frame, and to ask her subsequently to support her offspring, is a certain means of retarding her growth, if it does not also enfeeble her constitution. Those who care to take the risk of putting mares to the stud at two years of age, should at least exercise some judgement in the selection of subjects for the purpose.

They should be forward in growth, and at the same time well furnished for their age, and in good condition. They should not come to the stallion until late in the season, and from the very beginning should receive special dietary consideration throughout pregnancy and on through weaning.

An open yard, with a well-littered shed for protection,

11

and a run out in the course of the day if convenient, are the most suitable conditions for winter quarters.

It is in the interest of the race, no less than the breeder, that mares should not commence their stud career until they are four years old, when growth is being completed, and when the organs of reproduction have reached their full development, and the physiological energy of the system if disengaged from the task of building up the frame, and can be more effectually devoted to maturing the fetus.

HEREDITARY DEFECTS

The great bane of the breeding-stud--hereditary defects-must be jealously guarded against, and in this connection much assistance may be derived from the careful study of family history.

It should, however, be kept in mind that many ailments are acquired as the result of accident, which in their outward form are indistinguishable from those which are hereditary.

Sprains, curbs, ring-bone, side-bones, roaring, whistling, string-halt, shivering, and cataracts are of the many hereditary affections to which horses are liable, and whenever they appear, heredity should be suspected, unless evidence to the contrary is forthcoming.

A description of hereditary defects can be found in *Genetics of the Horse,* by Jones and Bogart. In chapter nine of that book can be found three charts and some photographs showing these defects. These defects have been described as lethals of varying sorts; true lethals, delayed lethals, and partial lethals. True lethals are described as causing death of the foal shortly before or shortly after birth. Delayed lethals are listed as those not generally causing death until sometime later in life. Partial lethals are less serious abnormalities that would cause death only in extreme circumstances.

THE MARE IN FOAL

Not the least important branch of stud-management is that which deals with the care and protection of mares during the period of pregnancy. A considerable percentage of the sickness and mortality ordinarily prevailing in our breeding-studs results from causes of a common and preventable char-

acter. Of these, some are especially conspicuous, and perhaps
none more so than the prevailing and rapidly-extending system of undue feeding, fattening, and pampering, to which
mares are usually subjected in the course of their show career.

This is an evil so obvious to anyone concerned in horse-
breeding, and so universally admitted by all, that neither evidence nor argument is called for here. The obesity in which
the great bulk of our show mares are found during the exhi-
bition season is a state altogether inconsistent with the exercise of the full measure of their productive powers. With
every organ in the body encumbered with fat and impeded
in function to the verge of disease, it would be strange indeed
if the fetus did not suffer in point of size and constitution.
Nor does the mischief of this injurious practice end here, for
the danger to both dam and foal where any impediment to
parturition arises is multiplied manifold, firstly by dimin-
ishing the room naturally available for the passage of the
fetus, and secondly by lowering the vitality and strength of
the dam, and adding to the difficulty of delivery. It is not
only in these immediate effects that this practice proves
harmful, but long after it has been discontinued, sterility or a
disposition to abort--one or the other--is often left behind.

Good general health is unquestionably the bodily condition most conducive to productiveness in the dam and
growth in the young, and this state can only be acquired and
maintained in its fullest measure by a judicious system of
liberal feeding and apportionment of suitable exercise. It
must, however, be recognized that while the former may, and
should, be within the reach of all who aspire to horse-
breeding, the latter is, for obvious reasons, impossible of
universal adoption. Mares kept exclusively for breeding purposes lead a life of idleness-in what is usually but erroneously
regarded as a natural state.

Of still greater importance to the well-being of the
brood-mare is the nature of the soil from which she draws
her sustenance. That best adapted to stud purpose is such
as will neither fatten nor starve, but supply a steady growth
of herbage of a sound and nutritive character throughout the
greater portion of the year. Low-lying, damp situations, where
the grass comes sour and rank, where the soil is wet, and
dense fogs prevail in the cold nights of spring and autumn,

are alike conducive to abortion and prejudical to health. When the grass supply becomes sparce a mare may begin to develop an appetite for certain noxious weeds growing in the pasture, most certainly leading to abortion. At all times the winter grazing of pregnant mares needs considerable care and attention on the part of the manager, and the resort to dry, nourishing diet should not be too long delayed. When it should be commenced will depend upon the nature and quality of the herbage, the size of the pasture, the number of stock upon it, the state of the season, and above all, upon the condition of the mares. The last-named should never be allowed to get low. Poverty on grass is the worst form of poverty, not only because it is usually attended with exposure, but also because of the tendency which the cold indifferent herbage of the autumn and winter possesses of lowering the temperature of the body. This kind of treatment not only predisposes to abortion, but at the same time retards the development of the fetus, and tends to impair its vitality and render the foal an easy prey to any disease that may overtake it at birth.

MARE NUTRITION DURING GESTATION

Crooked legs are perhaps the most dreaded mishap with which the horse breeder is concerned. There are so many uncontrollable factors, such as injuries and heredity, that the development of straight legs should not be left up to chance if we are to produce a perfect colt. Rickets and many types of arthritis, as well as crooked legs, can develop from a faulty diet of the mare while she is carrying the foal. For many years so much knowledge was lacking as to nutrition that horsemen were forced to rely solely on their pasture, hay and grain, hoping that all nutrients required would be supplied therein. Some breeders seem to have more trouble with crooked legs than others. Some have more trouble with foal diseases, and others don't seem to be plagued with many problems at all. Much of the reason for this can be traced back to the feed used by these various breeders. Calcium, phosphorus and vitamin D imbalance seem to be the main factors involved in most cases of crooked legs of a foal. Of course, even a breeder with these three factors in proper amounts

May have a crooked foal   now and then.

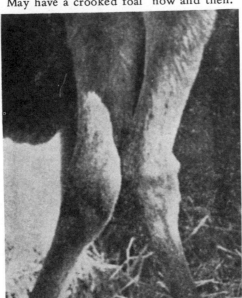

may have a crooked foal now and then, but year after year he is bound to have a much lower percentage of crookedness.

In this day and age, everyone is somewhat aware of the importance of calcium and phosphorus. However, most horseman are under the impression that their feedstuff contains adequate amounts, and if not, the addition of about any kind of mineral will do the job. The body has wonderful powers of adjustment when it comes to storing and utilizing calcium and phosphorus, but in too many cases this power is overtaxed and formation of the bones suffers. A fact that is little known or understood is that calcium and phosphorus must be supplied in a proper ratio in the diet of the horse. There is approximately twice as much calcium in the body as phosphorus. Unless the feed contains the same ratio of two to one, it is tied up to such an extent that the horse cannot utilize it. The ratio must not necessarily be in a mathematical exactness. Because the body has powers of adjustment, a ratio ranging anywhere from one to two parts of calcium for every part of phosphorus is sufficient. Actually, a proper supply of these minerals to the bones and tissue depends not only upon an adequate supply of them in the diet and the ratio as mentioned, but also the presence of vitamin D. With an abundant supply of vitamin D, the ratio of calcium and phosphorus takes on less meaning. With an abundant supply of vitamin D, more efficient utilization is made of the amounts of calcium and phosphorus present. Practically the only natural source of this vitamin for the horse is good old fashioned sunshine. The ultraviolet rays landing on the body of the horse are turned into vitamin D. The skin contains a substance called a "pro-vitamin" which, when activated by these short waves of light, (termed ultraviolet rays) are changed into vitamin D. These pro-vitamins seem to be in more abundance on the skin of a light colored horse. This may account for the belief of some people that crooked legs occur most commonly in foals from dark colored mares.

With the realization that vitamin D is perhaps the most important factor in the prevention of rickets and other bone deformities, it would be well for the breeder to examine the factors which effect the supply of it to their horses. Sunlight through ordinary window glass doesn't supply enough ultraviolet rays to produce vitamin D. The atmosphere surrounding our earth, filters out ultraviolet rays somewhat as a window glass does. The less atmosphere that is penetrated, the more ultraviolet rays will get through. In the winter, here in the northern hemisphere, the sun is never directly over head. The rays must travel through much more atmosphere before reaching our horses. We would expect to find very little vitamin D produced in horses in the far north in the winter. Also, using the same reasoning, sunlight during early morning or evening would contain little ultraviolet value. Horses that are stabled during the mid-day hours during the winter will miss practically all the ultraviolet potential in the sunshine. Even those horses pastured outside continually in the more northern latitudes will usually develop a short supply of vitamin D in the winter. This merits some consideration by the breeder because of the fact that these months are also the most crucial time for the pregnant mare. Some breeders have found the use of vitamin D supplement to be of help. There is very little vitamin D value in any horse feed. Some green sun-cured leafy alfalfa hay has a small amount. Nutritionists say it will contain 300 to 1000 units per pound, but very little work has been done to determine how many units are actually needed by the horse. Usually no more than one-half the diet of a horse is alfalfa and many breeders have no alfalfa available at all. Where a vitamin D deficiency is suspected the feeding of a few alfalfa pellets each day might be beneficial.

One of the most important considerations involved with the amount of vitamin D needed is the ratio of calcium to phosphorus in the diet. If our hay and grain contain 10 times more calcium than phosphorus, much vitamin D is utilized in the body process of converting these minerals to bone. And vice versa, if we feed 10 times more phosphorus than calcium, much more vitamin D will be used. By feeding a ration with approximately twice as much calcium as phosphorus, very little vitamin D is used, and even though the mare has insufficient sunlight, her supply of vitamin D may last through the winter.

Farms within the same county may very considerably as to the amounts of these minerals. Some feed companies will, without much charge, run a feed analysis on a sample of your hay. In this manner, a breeder can determine exactly

Some feed companies will, without much charge, run a feed analysis on a sample of your hay.

how much calcium and phosphorus is needed, if any, as a supplement.

Less trouble is apt to occur in an area deficient in calcium than one deficient in phosphorus. Most roughages fed to horses contain more calcium than phosphorus even if the area is deficient in calcium. Perhaps the best mineral supplement which would give an extra supply of phosphorus would be di-calcium phosphate. It is available from most feed companies. One or two of the better feed companies are marketing mineral supplements that are balanced for their particular area. They can vary the calcium and phosphorus in their supplement depending upon what is needed.

Some breeders feel that a deficiency in phosphorus can be made up with the feeding of wheat bran and other grains. This is not usually the case. Take for instance a typical diet for a broodmare, in an area with normal calcium and phosphorus in the soil. "Feeds and Feeding" recommends the use of three pounds of bran, three pounds of oats and one pound of linseed meal, each day along with 16 pounds of timothy hay. This combination would supply three and one-half parts of calcium for every part of phosphorus. This is because the hay supplies a much greater percentage of calcium than the grain does phosphorus. Of course, if the hay were grown in a calcium deficient area, this diet would approach the more desirable ratio of two parts calcium to one part phosphorus. In a normal area it would take eight gallons of oats to supply enough phosphorus to bring the ratio to 2:1. Or by using bran, which is higher in phosphorus than oats, this ratio could be obtained with only one gallon for each sixteen pounds of hay. A more desirable grain supplement which would supply the same amount of phosphorus would be one-half gallon of bran and four and one-half gallons of oats. Because of these large amounts of grains required we can see that in most cases this just wouldn't be practical. The feeding of show horses might be the only exception.

In most instances di-calcium phosphate supplement will adequately supply the phosphorus needed. It has been estimated that one pound of timothy hay contains .001 oz. of excess calcium. If a mare were to eat as much as 30 pounds in one day she would receive .03 oz. excess. It has also been estimated that 1/4 oz. of di-calcium phosphate will supply .015 oz. more phosphorus than needed. This would balance the ratio bringing it pretty close to 2:1. There is an excellent preparation of di-calcium phosphate which can be obtained from almost any veterinarian. It contains vitamin D and an iodide compound which helps in combating bacterial infections.

It is very seldom that we see a colt, born sickly and puny, go on to be a great performance horse. Of course it does happen, but the odds are certainly against it. This is why we need to do all we can to see that the foal is born healthy. No doubt one of the main factors determining the health of a new foal is the proper diet of his dam during gestation. Outside of vitamin and mineral deficiency, probably a deficiency of protein is of most common concern. This protein can be supplied with the use of one-half clover or alfalfa along with timothy hay, plus one and one-half gallons of oats. Probably about the only time we would have to worry about a deficiency in the horse would be if the diet were composed of strictly dry grass hay.

Vitamin A is essential to the broodmare during gestation. A severe lack of it can go so far as to cause the mare to abort her foal. Without this vitamin, bones of the fetus cannot develop straight. It is somehow tied up in the process of bone development. An adequate supply helps give the foal, when it is born, a resistance to diseases. It has been found that respiratory troubles tend to be more severe without proper amounts of the vitamin. Attacks of distemper which are often a big problem in young foals can be less of a problem with plenty of vitamin A in the diet of the broodmare.

Perhaps the best source of vitamin A to our horses is good green pasture. However, very few mares have the advantage of green pastures during late gestation. Good green alfalfa hay would usually supply an adequate amount of the vitamin. About the only time a breeder might run into a vitamin A deficiency would be during the late winter when on a ration of strictly dry timothy hay with no green color.

It has been found that vitamin A can be stored for months in the system. Therefore a vitamin A shortage would have to be prolonged over a period of several months in most cases in order to bring about any adverse effects. Aside from vitamin supplements, alfalfa pellets would perhaps be the best source of vitamin A. Some breeders mix a pound a day with the daily grain ration of each mare when the only hay fed is dry timothy.

Our knowledge as to the importance of the B vitamins in the horse is lacking. We know that most all of them are synthesized by the bacteria in the intestinal tract. Grains and alfalfa hay are rich in almost all of the B vitamins and because of these two factors we see very little B vitamin deficiency. At least it is not identified as such.

Research also needs to be done on the needs and uses of vitamin E. It is associated with the reproduction process in rats. However, we are not certain of its complete function in the horse. It is supplied commonly in most hays and grains and is almost impossible to develop a deficiency of it in the horse. It may very well be that as we learn more about vitamins and their uses in horses, we may come to recognize some of our present day ailments caused to some degree by a vitamin deficiency.

THE PREGNANT MARE

It seems that nothing conduces so much to the production of strong, healthy offspring as giving the mare a reasonable amount of work, under judicious management. A certain element of risk, it is true, always attends the over work of pregnant animals, and especially those engaged in farmwork, but with common care this is far outweighed by the benefits conferred on the dam and produce. When mares have well-proportioned exercise and a liberal supply of good food, foals are not only dropped bigger and stronger, but they resist the exposure to adverse influences, and thrive and grow much better than those from idle, ill-conditioned mares.

As to the stage of pregnancy when mares should cease to be ridden, different people entertain different ideas, but the question is surely far more one of management than of opinion. It is common enough for mares to be ridden rather heavily right up to the time of parturition, and especially among ranchers who need the services of the mare. Pregnant mares as a general rule are all the better off when ridden up to within three or four weeks of the time of foaling. In-foal mares should, however, be guarded against severe exertion, such as drawing heavy loads in deep ground or on hilly roads, or backing, or trotting at fast pace, especially down hill, nor should they be made to undergo long fasts or suffer fatigue. As pregnancy advances, and the calls of the growing fetus on the nutritive resources of the dam become more and more considerable, so should the amount of exercise demanded of her be diminished, and the food-ration undergo suitable adjustment.

In the stable, pregnant mares should be provided with plenty of room to permit them to lie down and extend themselves over a good bed of soft litter. The floor of the stable should not slant too much in a backward direction. When separated by bails, their companions should be quiet and free from vice. Breeding-mares, however, never perhaps do better than when turned into the crew yard at night, with a dry shed for protection from the weather, and plenty of dry litter, providing they are on good terms with each other. Cold and changeable climate has often been urged against this exposure of pregnant mares, but experience teaches that, with an adequate food-supply, the open yard is far more conducive to health than the atmosphere of the average stable, which is usually made filthy by the studious exclusion of outside air and the deliberate confinement. Moreover, the denizens of the open yard know nothing of those extremes of temperature, the sudden alternations of which are so fruitful of disease.

When the weather permits, this kind of management allows of the mare's being turned to grass for a few hours each day during the later weeks of pregnancy, without the risk attaching to animals more closely stabled. A bite of spring grass, before parturition, prepares for the more complete change of food which is shortly to take place, and protects the foal from those often fatal attacks of diarrhea, which result when mares are suddenly transferred from hard corn to pasture--from the close stable to the open field.

WHEN FOALS SHOULD FALL

To regulate the mating of mares so that the foals will be dropped at a suitable season should be a matter of great concern to the breeder. In these days of horse shows, with their numerous and costly prizes, medals, and championships, great temptation is offered to the breeder of pedigree stock to strive for early produce, and resort to a system of forcing and pampering which, while productive of a limited and temporary success, cannot be otherwise than disastrous to the general well-being of the horse. As to the particular month of the year when foals should be encouraged to come, a great deal will depend upon the soil, locality, and climate in which they are to be reared, and naturally, opinions on this question vary with the variations of experience gained under different local conditions. In areas of uncertain climate, early foaling is distinctly prejudicial to the life and health of the offspring, and it is not too much to say that a large share of the loss and disappointment that breeders experience under ordinary conditions is due to this cause. Some consider the advantage of an early colt to be a good set-off against the risk entailed, and the latter part of February or the beginning of March is the time arranged for foaling to commence.   With the prevailing winds from the west or

Foals should be dropped at a suitable season.

north-west at this season of the year, cold rains and snow-storms, little sunlight, and a scanty supply of rank herbage, both mare and foal must either be subjected to confinement for several weeks, or face the rigours of the season and attendant risks. Nothing conduces so much to the health and well-being of the dam, and to the growth and stability of the foal in the first period of its life, as an abundance of spring grass and sunshine. These considerations have led many breeders to move their operations to the southern parts of the country. In some cases this has been worth-while, but it is often found that many other problems com-plicate the early foaling prospects of sunny Arizona or Florida.

All things considered, the best foaling time occurs in late March or April. Through May and June the best and strongest foals will be dropped, and most successfully reared. The best food that can be produced, and the most perfect stable and management that can be designed, are poor sub-stitutes for the liberty, pure air, and rich succulant herbage of advanced spring.

Dry soil, temperate climate, and a protected site, are the most con-genial to early produce.

Foals dropped late in the summer are at an equal disadvantage with those that appear too early. The grass at this time is losing its goodness, and the milk of the dam is indifferent both in quality and quantity. Besides, the nights are getting cold and damp, and, worse than everything, the youngster will be shedding its coat at a time when it should possess its winter suit. All this tends to lower the vitality of the individual, to check growth, and hamper development. If foals are to grow, and shape, and make good horses, they must bask in the sunshine of summer, and receive an abundant supply of the rich milk and ripe herbage it affords. Moreover, growth, to be attended with substantial development, must be continuous, and uninterrupted by the poverty and inclemency of both spring and autumn.

Light land districts where the soil is dry, the climate temperate, and the site protected, are the most congenial to early produce, but under the most favorable conditions early foals should only be turned out when the sun shines, and where shelter, in the shape of a comfortable shed, is provided.

III. FOAL CARE

The bowels of the foal at birth contain a considerable amount of fecal matter, consisting of the solid remains of bile, and other secretions thrown out by the mucous membrane of the intestines during development. Usually this is discharged soon after birth as a soft greenish or yellowish brown substance known as meconium. In some cases, this material becomes hard and dry, and not discharged without an enema being administered.

The foal is noticed to keep raising the tail, arching the back, and posing as if to dung, and now and again straining without effect. Warm soapy water may be injected into the bowel, by means of a soft flexible rubber tube, two or three

A group of healthy weanlings

25

times during the day. Should this fail to effect removal of its contents, a veterinarian should be called without delay. If the constipation becomes habitual in the foal, the dam must be allowed an extra supply of carrots or green food, and the addition of bran to her daily grain.

Foals, when born before the full term of gestation, are sometimes discharged enveloped in the fetal membranes or after-birth, and, as they are then disconnected from the dam, respiration is only possible by exposure to the external air; it is necessary, therefore, that the membranes be promptly removed. This having been done, breathing may be set in motion by a little artificial respiration, sprinkling the face with cold water, or shaking the foal in the air by its hind legs.

It is of the first importance that the after-birth be promptly removed from the box and buried in some un-frequented place, and sufficiently deep to guard against its being exhumed by dogs.

The milk of mares which foal prematurely is always scant and of indifferent quality for the first two or three days, and may require to be supplemented by milk from another mare or from the cow.

The raw edges of the broken umbilical cord will serve as an entrance area for infectious organisms into the system of the foal if it is not properly disinfected immediately. A strong tincture of iodine (7%) is generally painted over the umbilicus. Unless this procedure is followed routinely, navel or joint ill may result, which will seriously hamper the growth and development of the foal.

At the time of birth and for some time afterwards, foals often present an unshapely and awkward appearance. Their hocks or knees, or both, are acutely flexed, and their fetlocks may almost touch the ground. The limbs give the impression of being incapable of supporting the weight of the body. It should, however, be remembered that where there is no bending of bones, or shortening of ligaments or tendons, the foal invariably 'straightens up', and the deformity gradually disappears as growth proceeds. In those cases where the bending of the joints is due to contraction of the tendons, the defect may be remedied by mechanically stretching or dividing the latter by a surgical operation.

FOALS PREMATURELY BORN

When foals come before their time, they lack the finishing touch in the work of development, although every organ may be fully represented in all its parts and relations. The prospect of rearing these immature youngsters will depend upon the period of gestation which has been reached when they are born, and the strength and vitality they display at the time.

In all cases they require the greatest attention and care, and in some, however anxious we may be to preserve life, the task is hopeless from the first. This is especially so when birth takes place four or five weeks before the natural period.

Foals prematurely born are, from their ill-developed condition, small, and being too weak to stand, are unable to feed themselves. They display a great desire for sleep, and it is of the first importance that every encouragement be given to its restorative influence. For some time the breathing will be more or less quick, and to the uninitiated may give the idea of some grave lung disease, but under judicious management a gradual subsidence will take place as time goes on, until the normal standard of breathing is reached.

Being helpless, a foal prematurely born should be removed from the presence of the mare as soon as it has been thoroughly cleansed, and conveyed into a warm, dry area, where, if necessary, artificial heat must be supplied.

Laid on a soft bed of hay, and covered by a couple of blankets, it should be left undisturbed for half to three-quarters of an hour, when the mare must be milked, and the produce given to the foal out of a feeding-bottle. This must be repeated every half-hour, with the precaution that the vessel used for receiving milk from the mare and the one employed in feeding the foal should be thoroughly scalded, drained, and dried in the oven each time after being used. Before the mare is milked, the teats and udder must be cleansed, and sponged over with a disinfectant.

Unless these precautions are strictly observed, and the milk conveyed fresh to the foal directly as it leaves the dam, it will be impossible to guard against diarrhea, and when this disease is once established in these imperfectly developed youngsters, a fatal termination is generally the result.

Hand-feeding will require to be continued night and day, every hour or so, until the foal is strong enough to feed itself, but after the first thirty-six hours the period between meals may be gradually extended.

When it has acquired sufficient strength to support itself, it may be returned to the dam. How it will be received by her is a question which must not be overlooked, and the attendant should stand by until the mare has settled down to her offspring and shows a desire to nurse it.

If, as is most likely to be the case, the dam is short of milk, the deficiency must be made up by a milk substitute as discussed later.

Isoerythrolysis is a hemolytic disease of foals which develops as a result of serum antibodies of the mare destroying the red blood cells of the foals. In many respects it is like the "yellow baby disease" in humans caused by the Rh factor. The equine blood antigens and antibodies which are responsible for isoerythrolysis have not as yet been determined. It is quite probable that various antigens of the horse may initiate the disease.

In some cases antigens in the foal's blood pass through the placental membranes, gaining entrance to the mare's blood. If any of these antigens are unlike those of the mare's, her system will be stimulated into a production of antibodies against them. Evidently, the antibodies are such large molecules that they cannot pass through the placental membrane into the fetal blood. Therefore, fetal red blood cells are not destroyed, and consequently the foal is born healthy.

During the latter stages of gestation the antibodies build up in the mare's blood, and also begin to accumulate in the udder. The mare's milk is therefore saturated with the antibodies. If the foal is allowed to nurse, the antibodies are quickly absorbed into its circulatory system. As a result the red blood cells are destroyed in large numbers, and icterus and anemia develops, followed generally by death.

A mare cannot produce antibodies against a foreign antigen upon first exposure. The initial exposure to the antigen is known as sensitization. Once this has occurred, the next exposure results in the production of antibodies. It may be that most of the antigens of the foal's blood do not normally gain entrance to the mare's blood, which would mean that a mare becomes sensitized only under unusual circumstances. Abnormal placental attachments which occasionally occur could allow antigens to pass. Blood transfusions could sensitize a mare, as well as the use of vaccine containing the antigen. The fact that sensitization occurs only occasionally explains why isoerythrolysis is rare.

It has become a common practice to test a mare's serum for antibodies which might destroy the foal's red blood cells, in cases were isoerythrolysis is suspected. This can be done in the latter stages of pregnancy.

When isoerythrolysis is suspected or confirmed, the foal should not be allowed to nurse initially. After "milking out" the mare in hourly intervals for 8 to 16 hours, it is usually safe for the foal to nurse.

HAND-REARING OF FOALS

It sometimes happens that the udder of the dam is functionally destroyed, or so far damaged as to be incapable of producing a supply of wholesome milk, or the dam may die and leave the offspring to be reared by foster-mothers or by hand.

To procure a foster-mother is always a difficult task, and sometimes a most costly one. It does, however, now and again occur that a mare will lose her foal, and a foal will lose its mother, about the same time and in these cases it is a mutual, if unequal, advantage to the persons concerned to bring the survivors together. When this can be done, the trouble is in a large measure removed, although it must be admitted that the transference of a newly-born foal to a strange mare is not unlikely to be attended with digestive disorder and diarrhea at first, and especially if the former has not received the first laxative milk of its dam, and the latter should have foaled several days prior to entering upon her fostering duties.

As to whether hand-rearing is a desirable course to pursue, this will very much depend on the age, character, and breeding of the offspring. The more youthful it is when deprived of its parent the greater amount of trouble it will give, whether its other properties be good, bad, or indifferent; and those who undertake the task of ministering to the wants of these unfortunate youngsters must be prepared for no little sacrifice of time, comfort, inconvenience and expense.

Failing a foster-mother, another source of food-supply is the cow. Here again some consideration must be given to selection of a suitable subject whence to obtain the milk, for if the task of hand-rearing is to be undertaken, it must be entered upon and pursued in such a way as to safeguard success at all points.

The most suitable milk for this purpose will be obtained from a heifer a week after calving, or if the foal has not sucked its dam it would be an advantage to procure a supply for the first thirty-six hours from a cow just calved, in order to awaken the action of the bowels and provoke discharge of their contents.

Once having commenced with the milk of a particular animal, it is most desirable that no change be made, if possible to guard against it, and, as we have previously observed, the milk of a young cow freshly calved is much to be preferred to that of a stale old one.

Although, as will be seen from the figures given below, the same constituents are found in the milk of the cow as enter into that of the mare, the actual and relative proportions of these constituents differ to a considerable extent. To approximate the composition of the one to that of the other, and to render it more suitable to the requirements of the foal, water must be added to reduce the proportions of casein and fat, and at the same time the deficiency of sugar must be made up. At first the proportion of water to cow's milk should be one part of the former to two of the latter, but as time goes on one part to three will be found more to the purpose, and later water may be excluded altogether. The following figures are percentages:--

	Cow's Milk.	Mare's Milk.
Water	87·0	88·0
Fat	4·6	1·0
Casein	4·0	1·6
Sugar	3·8	8·9
Salts	0·6	0·5

Thus it will be seen that while the fat and casein of the cow's milk is largely in excess of that of the mare's, the sugar of the mare's milk far exceeds that of the cow's.

Cleanliness in the vessels used and the handling of the milk should be strictly observed, and, above all, its administration must be frequent and regular, both as regards quantity and time. At first half a pint should be given every half-hour, and gradually increased as time goes on, while the intervals between meals may be extended accordingly. It must be remembered that to be successful the indications of nature must be closely observed and acted upon. Neglect in this matter can have but one result, failure.

In commencing this system of rearing from birth, attention should be directed to the state of the bowels at the outset. Should the foal not have received the first milk of its dam, constipation is more than likely to exist, and should be corrected by the administration of a small dose of laxative prescribed by a veterinarian. Enemas may be helpful at this point. Where the milk of a newly-calved cow can be procured, its purgative properties may be sufficient to unload the bowels, in which case further interference becomes unnecessary.

FEEDING ORPHAN FOALS

Borden Chemical Company has developed, through years of experimentation and research, a product called Foal-Lac which as shown in the chart below contains all of the essential ingredients of mare's milk. To assure the foal of extra nutritional support. Foal-Lac contains a higher level than mare's milk of vitamins and minerals needed by the foal.

Guidelines, as outlined in their booklet *The Borden Guide to the Care and Feeding of Orphan and Early Weaned Foals*, are as follows: The foal should be fed 4 times per day (every 6 hours if possible) for the first week as an orphan. If the foal adapts well to the feeding schedule and handles the increases without difficulty, it may be changed to three-times-per-day feeding (every 8 hours if possible) during the second week. If the foal does not readily consume the increases in feeding, it should be continued on 4 feedings per day. Three feedings per day should be sufficient for the

Feeding orphan foals.

third week, and this can be reduced to 2 feedings per day during the fourth week. Finally the feedings should be reduced to 1 per day a couple of days prior to discontinuing liquid feeding.

Directions on the container outline two different feeding schedules. One of these should be used with a ration formulated for young foals containing a minimum of 16% protein supplemented with vitamins and minerals. The second one should be used with a simple grain mixture or a low-protein horse feed. These feeding schedules including the introduction of Foal-Lac pellets and the grain ration should be self explanatory and are discussed briefly below.

Feeding liquid Foal-Lac in an open bucket will probably bring the most success. To start the foal, rub a little on its mouth and place its nose in the milk. It sometimes helps to hold the bucket for the foal until it starts to drink. Then lead it to the permanent feeding area with the bucket. The bucket should be placed about the height of the foals shoulders and tipped slightly toward the foal so that all the milk can be readily consumed. The foal may require 1 or 2 hours to drink the milk during the first couple of days.

FOAL-LAC AND MARE'S MILK

Ingredient	Mare's Milk (Solids Basis)	Foal-Lac
Protein (%)	19.6%	20.2%
Fat	14.2%	14.4%
Fiber	0.0%	0.2%
Milk Sugar (Lactose)	53.4%	52.6%
Ash	3.6%	7.2%
Calcium	0.9%	0.9%
Phosphorus	0.5%	0.8%
Cobalt	----------	1.1 mg./lb.
Copper	----------	14.6 mg./lb.
Iodine	----------	0.8 mg./lb.
Iron	----------	57.8 mg./lb.
Magnesium	400.0 mg./lb.	501.0 mg./lb.
Manganese	----------	24.0 mg./lb.
Potassium	0.5%	1.6%
Sodium	0.18%	0.8%
Zinc	----------	20.3 mg./lb.
Vitamin A	1818.0 U.S.P. Units/lb.	10,500.0 U.S.P. Units/lb.
Vitamin D $_2$	varies	2,100.0 U.S.P. Units/lb.
Vitamin E	----------	2.5 Int. Units/lb.
Vitamin K	----------	2.0 mg./lb.
Thiamine	1.2 mg./lb.	2.4 mg./lb.
Riboflavin	0.8 mg./lb.	9.2 mg./lb.
Pantothenic Acid	12.1 mg./lb.	17.0 mg./lb.
Pyridoxine	1.2 mg./lb.	2.4 mg./lb.
Niacin	2.0 mg./lb.	5.2 mg./lb.
Choline	----------	636.0 mg./lb.
Folic Acid	4.0 mcg./lb.	266.0 mcg./lb.
Biotin	----------	13.0 mg./lb.
Vitamin B $_{12}$	12.1 mcg./lb.	11.6 mcg./lb.
Ascorbic Acid	404.0 mg./lb.	454.0 mg./lb.

Wash the bucket in hot, soapy water after each feeding. Rinse thoroughly and invert the bucket so that it dries before the next feeding.

Consult your veterinarian if there are any signs of disease, fever, parasites, etc. A worming program should be established even for a young foal to keep it free from parasites.

Foals less than one week old should be out of the weather, especially at night. A heat lamp in the stall is desirable if the foal is orphaned during the first 3 days of life and especially if foaling occurred in cold weather. Place the lamp in such a position that the foal can get away if it becomes uncomfortable. If it is doing well, the lamp can be removed after the first week.

At the start of the second week, some grain or a special complete foal ration should be offered. If may be desirable to place a couple of handfuls of good-quality, heavy rolled oats in the feeding box along with the grain mixture or complete foal ration. Foals generally like rolled oats, and the oats will encourage them to start eating the grain ration. If the grain is not consumed in 2 days, remove it from the box and offer fresh feed. The foals can be allowed to eat all the grain ration they want providing there are no problems with stool consistency. They may be eating 1 to 2 pounds per day by the time they are 1 month old.

During the third week Foal-Lac pellets should be introduced and mixed with the grain ration. Just add a small handful at first until the foals eat the pellets readily. As the Foal-Lac powder is descreased on the 30-day liquid schedule, Foal-Lac pellets should be increased so that by the time liquid feeding is discontinued, or shortly thereafter, the foals are receiving 2 pounds of Foal-Lac pellets per day. If the 8-week liquid feeding schedule is followed. Foal-Lac pellets should be fed at the rate of 1 pound per day until the 50th day. Then increase Foal-Lac pellets to replace the powder as it is reduced so that the foal receives 2 pounds of pellets per day by the 60th day.

Good-quality, dust-free alfalfa hay should be made available at about 3 weeks of age. This is particularly important if pasture is not available or if alfalfa is not included in the grain ration. If the foals consume too much hay or they seem to get diarrhea from the hay, grass hay should be substituted.

Provide fresh water starting the second week. A salt block may be used, particularly if a home-mixed grain ration is used. A complete foal feed will probably provide adequate salt.

Foals should be exercised daily. After they are 1 to 2 weeks old, depending on their condition and the weather, they can have free access to pasture as long as there is a protected feeding area and a place they can go for shelter from rain and wind.

Foals orphaned during the second or third week of life will be 20 to 30 pounds heavier than the foals orphaned during the first week unless they have not received sufficient milk from the mare or the mare's milk distressed the foal. If the foal is in a weakened condition, follow the directions for younger foals outlined above. Otherwise start the foal on 1 pound level of Foal-Lac powder for 1 or 2 days. If the foal readily consumes this and shows no digestive disturbances due to diet change (from mare's milk to Foal-Lac), the foal can be brought up to 1.5 pounds and then 2 pounds of

Good-quality, dust-free alfalfa hay should be made available at about 3 weeks of age . . .

Foal-Lac powder over a period of a couple of days. The schedule can then be picked up for a 3 week old foal as shown in the detailed feeding schedules. These foals can start right off on a 3-times-per-day feeding frequency.

Foals that have been with the mare as long as 2 weeks are often more difficult to get on Foal-Lac. Do not be disturbed if they do not readily consume all the Foal-Lac liquid. Introduce them as soon as possible to grain and Foal-Lac pellets and encourage them to drink as much Foal-Lac liquid as they will consume up to the 2 pounds of powder per day.

Foals orphaned after 1 month with the mare or intentionally weaned from the mare at this age are sometimes reluctant to drink liquid Foal-Lac. The foals should be offered liquid Foal-Lac at a level of 1 pound of Foal-Lac powder per day divided into 2 feedings. If the foal readily consumes this, it can be increased to 2 pounds of powder after 1 or 2 days and continued for 7 to 10 days or until the foal is adjusted to living without the mare. The liquid feeding at this age serves to bridge the gap from mare to dry feed, although it is not required for the production of a strong healthy animal.

During this time the orphaned foal should be encouraged to start eating the grain ration, Foal-Lac pellets and hay so that it can be on a dry feed program within the week or 10 days mentioned above.

There are several reasons why it may be desirable to wean the foal as early as 1 month of age from the mare. Some of these are a desire to show the mare, fewer problems with returning the mare to the stable for personal or commercial riding, sale of mare or foal without the sale of the other, and ease of shipping mare (without foal) for breeding purposes. If you plan to wean early, the foal feeding program should be designed so that it can be accomplished with a minimum of effort.

After the foal is 1 week old, it should be tied at the feeding trough with the mare to encourage the foal to eat the grain ration. Again, some rolled oats may encourage the consumption of the mixed feed. Place some feed in the foal's mouth, so it can become acquainted with this new experience. Starting during the second week put a small quantity of Foal-

Lac pellets in the feeding area where the foal is tied so it will also be familiar with this feed.

Foals will vary greatly in their aggressiveness at the feed trough. Some will start eating dry feed at the first exposure while others may not eat very much even by the time they are 4 weeks old. If a foal does start to eat dry feed readily, it will help the weaning process to tie the foal away from the mare at feeding time and give it access to its own feed.

When the time comes for weaning (4 to 6 weeks of age), the break should be complete. Do not try to bring the mare and foal together for periodic nursing or the foal will not eat readily and both the mare and foal will be nervous. The mare and foal should be separated both from sight and hearing if at all possible. They will try to get together for a couple of days especially if they can see and hear each other. This could result in management problems.

Make sure the early weaned foal has fresh water. It is desirable to feed a special foal feed with a minimum of 16% protein and fortified with vitamins and minerals. The milk nutrients will be provided by the pelleted Foal-Lac. The Foal-Lac should be brought up to 2 pounds per day as soon as possible. The feeding of liquid Foal-Lac as discussed above will ease the transition. Note the table for suggested feeding schedules utilizing either a complete, specially designed foal ration or a mixture of grains or low-protein horse feed.

Foals that are weaned at 4 weeks or older and occasionally foals orphaned after they are 2 or 3 weeks old will become nervous and may not eat well because they miss the company of the mare or other horses. Chances are there will be only one foal that is orphaned or has been early weaned at one time. To overcome this problem we suggest placing another farm animal or a gentle dog with the foal for companionship.

As the Foal-Lac liquid is increased there may be a tenporary stool looseness. If this gets very watery and persists for 24 hours, the Foal-Lac should be reduced to the original level for two days and then increased perhaps more slowly than indicated in the feeding directions. If the condition does not correct itself, the veterinarian should be consulted.

The hair around the foal's muzzle may be lost after a couple of weeks due to the contact with the liquid. This should not cause concern, as the hair returns normally when the foal is off liquid feed.

These feeding directions will result in good sound foals. Some may prefer to feed liquid Foal-Lac at higher levels and for longer periods than indicated, particularly if the foals are doing well and extra condition is desired. Some have fed 6 to 8 pounds of Foal-Lac powder mixed with the appropriate amount of water per day to foals that are 2 to 3 months old. These animals take on a fine condition and make excellent animals for sale or display. Foal-Lac powder mixed with water can be continued through 4 to 6 months in place of pellets if the owner prefers this approach.

The chart below gives the Borden schedule for mixing and feeding for light horses (900-1200 pounds mature weight). Ponies will require about one-half these quantities. Note that there are two sets of directions; the one to be followed will depend on the quality of the grain ration used.

Age of Foal	No. of Feedings Day of Liquid Foal-Lac**	Warm Water Pints	Total Daily Foal-Lac Powder, Lbs.*	Total Daily Foal-Lac Pellets, Lbs.
0-3 days	4 (4)	4 (4)	1 (1)	0
4 days	4 (4)	6 (6)	1.5 (1.5)	0
5 days	4 (4)	6 (6)	1.5 (1.5)	0
6 days	4 (4)	8 (8)	2.0 (2.0)	0
7 days	4 (4)	8 (8)	2.0 (2.0)	0
2nd week ***	3 (3)	8 (8)	2.0 (2.0)	0
3rd week	3 (3)	8 (8)	2.0 (2.0)	¼ (¼)
4th week	2 (3)	6 (10)	1.5 (2.5)	½ (½)
29 days	1 (2)	4 (10)	1.0 (2.5)	1 (1)
30 days	0 (2)	0 (12)	0 (3.0)	1 (1)
31-35 days	0 (2)	0 (12)	0 (3.0)	1½ (1)
6th week	0 (1)	0 (12)	0 (3.0)	2 (1)
7th week	0 (1)	0 (8)	0 (2.0)	2 (1)
8th week	0 (1)	0 (4)	0 (1.0)	2 (2)
9th-12th week	0 (0)	0 (0)	0 (0)	2 (2½)
13th-16th week	0 (0)	0 (0)	0 (0)	1 (2½)
17th - 20th week	0 (0)	0 (0)	0 (0)	½ (1)
21st-24th week	0 (0)	0 (0)	0 (0)	½ (1)
Total Foal-Lac consumed in 6 months			50 (113)	169 (240)

*Three level cupfuls equal one pound

**Divide the total daily water and Foal-Lac powder allowance equally into the the number of feedings indicated.

***Start offering grain ration in small amounts. Fresh water should be made available at this time. Provide a small quantity of alfalfa hay unless the roughage is provided in the mixed grain ration or the foals are allowed access pasture. A salt block should be provided with a home-mixed grain or low-protein horse feed program.

SUPPLEMENTAL FEEDING OF THE FOAL

To supplement the milk of the mare with that of the cow or the use of a powdered supplement as a means of raising foals is in certain circumstances both desirable and necessary. Fillies with their first foal frequently fall short of an ample supply to keep the sucker growing, and especially is this the case after a hard winter on poor feed. At this early period of life the mare is building up her own frame at the same time that she is nourishing her offspring. The mammary gland has not yet reached its full size, and as a milk-making machine it has not developed a high functional activity.

Mares advanced in years before being put to the stud, as well as those which have bred on to the decline of life, and others constitutionally weak, frequently fail to yield the necessary amount of milk for the support of their offspring. The same result may follow upon an injury to the mammary gland, by which its functional activity becomes in a greater degree curtailed. Nor is the question of the nourishing power of the dam's milk always one of quantity, there may be a lack of quality.

In these circumstances a little help from a supplement, until the youngster can forage for itself, may make the difference between a valuable and a useless animal--between a serious loss and a substantial gain to the breeder. Continued use of excessive supplements long after weaning is sometimes maintained. There is no doubt that by this treatment a spurt is given to growth, size is materially increased, and so long as the allowance is continued and the balance of health upheld a vigorous growth is provoked and maintained--in other words the animal is 'forced'. It is in this way that many of the foals and yearlings that take champion rank at our various shows are built up. But how many fall victims by the way, and fail to realize the hopes and aspirations of the too ambitious owner, is only known even approximately to the veterinarian. Diseased feet, overshot joints, bog-spavins, and wind-galls, to say nothing of the constitutional break-down which some-times follows upon a discontinuance of the milk diet, are the too common consequences of this hurrying treatment.

It is not the intention of the writer to condemn the use of supplements in the rearing of foals where circumstances call for it, but to caution the breeder against its abuse, for when the ailments indicated above are brought into existence by this forcing system, they not only occasion immediate disappointment, but frequently continue, and result in deter-ioration and loss.

WEANING FOALS

The longer a foal can have the easily assimilable milk of its dam the better horse it will make. But mares are seldom permitted to wean their own foals, as they are soon put to the task of building up another fetus. Although a pregnant

Foals are usually weaned about September or October.

mare can nurse a foal, without ill effects either to parent or progeny, when pushed too far they are likely to prejudice the health of all concerned. As the fetus of the pregnant mare in-creases in size and attains to higher development, suckling can only be carried on at a disadvantage to the former, and a heavy drain on the nutritive resources of the latter.

Foals are usually weaned about September or October, when they are five or six months old. At this period of the year nights are getting cold and damp, pastures are on the wane, the milk-supply is falling away, and if the mare has been to service her fetus has made considerable growth and requires all her support.

Where, as the result of constitutional weakness or de-bility, from backward growth or any other cause, it is con-sidered desirable that the foal should continue with the dam for an extended period, then both should be allowed an ample supply of grain and any demand that is being made on the mare in regard to work should cease.

Animals when called upon to extend the period of suckling, should be taken up early and put into a well-littered yard, and have the protection of an open shed.

In all cases the foal should be well 'done' with grain and perhaps some type of supplement for three or four weeks before being weaned, so that the loss of the mother's milk may not be so severely felt.

As to whether the separation of the foal should be made completely at once, or by allowing it to return to the mare at increasing intervals, is a matter upon which breeders are not by any means unanimous, some adopting the one course and some the other, with equal success and satisfaction. Perhaps a gradual intermittent process of weaning is most rational, and best adapted to safeguard the health of both dam and offspring.

For some time after separation takes place the mamm-ary gland of the dam continues its secreting function, and in the case of mares in whom lactation is very active may cause painful distension of the udder. To avoid this, the quantity and milk-forming quality of the food supplied to the dam should be reduced, and only a moderate measure of water allowed.

Restlessness will be greatly appeased by two or more foals being turned out together.

After weaning, foals should not be allowed to 'go back' in condition, but should be kept growing by a liberal ration of manger food and good pasture.

The restlessness resulting from separation from the dam will be greatly appeased by company, and especially by two or more foals being turned out together.

THE MARE AFTER FOALING

To safeguard the foal it is necessary that every attention be given to the mare after parturition. Old matrons which have passed through the ordeal again and again, and are familiar with the duties of their office, seldom call for interference. With young mares, however, fresh to the business, certain special precautions require to be observed. In the first place, the teats should be examined as to their permeability. In some instances there is no opening for the escape of milk, and the foal pines, and is sometimes reduced to the verge of starvation before the defect is discovered.

So long as the excitement resulting from foaling continues, strangers should not be allowed access to the stables, and the man in attendance should be one who is best known to the mare, and who has been in the habit of feeding and tending her.

When the excitement of parturition has passed away, and the foal has gained its legs, it will soon commence to seek for the teat, and it may be sometimes desirable to direct it to the gland. This however, should not be attempted too soon, for the natural instinct of the little creature will sooner or later guide it to the source of its food-supply.

Young mares are liable to injure their foals by stepping upon them before they 'get their legs', but this is frequently brought about by the over-anxiety and untimely interference of the attendant. Strong foals quickly rise to their feet, and require but little interference. Weakly foals, on the other hand, or those prematurely born, make many ineffectual attempts to rise, and in doing so are liable to fall in the way of the dam and suffer injury. It is in these cases that special watchfulness and care are required. Here the attendant should allow the foal plenty of time, and wait until it is able of itself to rise. It may then be supported and assisted to the teat.

For the first twenty-four hours after foaling, the mare's diet should be carefully selected and adjusted as to quantity. At first, warm oatmeal or bran is the most suitable; and if parturition has been troublesome and prolonged, and there is evidence of exhaustion and weakness, a few ounces of whiskey could be mixed with it and repeated in two or three hours. A little scalded bran and crushed oats may follow, and later a liberal quantity of special supplement for lactating mares.

After the mare has cleansed and drained, the soiled straw should be removed from the foaling-box and the floor well swept and disinfected. For several days a certain small quantity of discharge will flow from the genital passage and soil the tail, and maybe the udder and teats, and in a putrid condition this may find its way into the stomach of the foal, and occasion diarrhea of an obstinate or even of a rapidly fatal character.

Many of those attacks of this disease of obscure origin, and which are attributed to all sorts of possible and impossible causes, arise out of the ingestion of decomposing filth, taken in the act of suckling. This poisonous stuff may also be transferred to the udder by the filth-laden tail, or be gathered from the sodden litter on which the mare may lie.

To avoid danger to the foal from this cause, the udder should be sponged from time to time during the first few days after parturition, and the tail of the dam should also be thoroughly washed and cleansed. These precautions are especially necessary in those cases where foaling has been difficult and has called for assistance, and the discharge has been considerable.

For the first two days after foaling, both mare and offspring should be protected from cold and wet, and especially from exposure to chilling winds. As the mare and foal will soon require to be turned out to grass, overheating of the stable must be strictly guarded against by free but carefully regulated ventilation. Neglect of these precautions may cause serious, if not fatal, pneumonia.

To keep a foaling-box too cold, is pardonable, to overheat it is dangerous. As soon as the weather permits, both mare and foal should go to grass. In turning them out for the first time, that part of the day should be selected when the sun is out, the wind in a favorable quarter and not too brisk, and when the ground is fairly dry. After confinement, foals in their gallops and gambols often become overheated, and in a state of fatigue throw themselves down on the wet, cold ground, or stand about in a biting wind, causing serious, if not fatal, consequences.

In the early spring the weather is prone to rapid and extreme changes, and bright warm sunlight is often followed by piercing winds and driving rains; and with these adverse forces to contend with, the careful studsman will arrange his first turn-out within easy reach of shelter and protection. This will not be needed long, for foals soon adapt themselves to an outdoor life.

Even when a turn-out is not desirable, foals should be provided with plenty of room to move about, and have in addition forced exercise under shelter of a shed. A little movement helps to straighten up a foal and put him fairly on his legs.

When the turn-out comes, the question will arise as to how far grass should be supplemented. This will, of course, depend a good deal upon the state of the weather, the nature of the soil, and the stage of growth of the herbage. Cold weather, with a shortage of grass, will call for a liberal daily ration of dry food.

Young mares which enter upon their maternal duties at three years old, and old ones whose yield of milk is insufficient, should always receive a couple of feeds of grain daily for two or three weeks after being turned out, or until the grass comes to its best.

In both these circumstances the foals should be encouraged to eat grain with the dam, so that any lack of milk-supply occurring as the season advances may be met by a further addition of a supplement of some type. Without this precaution the foals of young growing mares, and those of old ones whose vitality has been lowered by age and hard work, seldom make good growth and develop size and constitution.

Mares with foals at foot should have good range of pasture, and in addition an occasional change is most desire-able.

IV. STALLION CARE AND REPRODUCTION

Nothing is more important to the success of the breeding stud than a good sire, and to prolong and maintain his fertility can only be effected by scrupulous care and rational treatment, in which the aim should be to keep up the balance of health and render his sexual work fruitful.

It must, however, be remembered that fertility will differ in different animals, and in the same animal at different periods of life. The recognition of this fact suggests the desirability of regulating the work of a sire to his powers of service and reproduction, so that abuse may be avoided, his use at the stud prolonged, and the number and value of his produce enhanced.

Rightly or wrongly it is the common practice to allow a horse to commence his stud career at two years old, and, although no apparent ill consequences may follow when sexual work is judiciously apportioned, there is some evidence that at this critical period of growth some benefit would be derived by allowing another year to pass over, before calling upon him to exercise his reproductive function.

This precaution is especially needed where condition and growth are backward, or the system is wanting in strength and vigor. Big colts should be allowed ample time to develop before being put to the stud, and little ones to grow.

When it is decided to use a two-year-old colt, the natural question arises as to how many mares he should be allowed to have. The number of mares sometimes allowed to horses at this age is almost incredible. Some breeders think what a colt can do should be the measure of what he should do, and it is no rare occurrence for forty, fifty, or even sixty mares to receive service from these baby sires during their first season. That they may be fairly fruitful under such a strain has been sometimes shown, but the general result of such a practice

47

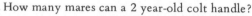

How many mares can a 2 year-old colt handle?

is not only to check growth and physical development, but to lay the foundation for sexual weakness and disappointment in the following season, and it may be, to produce a continuing weakness of the reproductive function, or even permanent incapacity to sire.

Having regard to health interest, to quality of produce, and endurance at the stud, a horse at the age in question should not be allowed more than ten to fifteen mares, and it would be much to his advantage, if the season were allowed to get well advanced before commencing service. At this time, grass will be plentiful and good, mares will 'come keen' to the horse, the chance of returning will be materially diminished, and the horse's services correspondingly lightened.

As to older stallions, the same want of care obtains with them as with the more juvenile section, and many a good horse is prematurely used up or falls a victim to disease as the outcome of unbridled abuse. The number of mares a horse should receive from three years old upwards allows of no fixed rule being laid down. Very much will depend upon growth and development, and even more on natural vigor of constitution and sexual capacity, which latter can only be known by experience. Some horses almost complete their upward growth at two years old, while others at that age have made but little progress.

In deciding the work load of young sires, every consideration should be given to their fitness in respect of the points referred to above, and lack in one respect or the other should be deemed sufficient to withhold them from stud service until, by time and good living, they have acquired the necessary growth and vigor of constitution to enable them to exercise the reproductive function without prejudice to their full development and maturation as sires.

There is a very wide difference in the desire and the capacity of horses for stud work. Some, although young and fairly fruitful, display a dismaying indifference towards their mares, and can only be induced to consummate the act by the greatest care, or some special device on the part of the groom. Many of these horses become more and still more indisposed for sexual connection, and ultimately refuse service altogether becoming prematurely impotent. In some the desire may be maintained by good living, plenty of walking exercise, iron tonics, vitamin supplements, and by keeping the horse away from mares for such a period as will bring back the sexual impulse. How long this may be, the attendant must find out for himself, and having done so, exercise his descretion in directing the services of the horses under his care. On the other hand, there are stallions which with a remarkable capacity for service unite an extraordinary fertility and endurance. A notable instance of this occurred some years ago by a well-known Shire stallion, which on completing a heavy season in Lancashire, was let for further work in the south. On reaching his destination, at three o'clock in the day, twenty-three mares were waiting for service. Of these, nineteen were found to be in season, and were served the same day. Thirteen of these later proved to be in foal.

Many sires, and some of great celebrity, have been known to serve from 200 to 260 mares in one season, and to leave a fair proportion of foals. Of course, it cannot be expected that such an amount of sexual work as is here implied can be continued for any number of years without inducing sterility or premature impotence, and owners of stallions, in their own interest, no less than that of their stock, should guard against dangerous abuse of their stallions by judicious restriction of their services at the stud.

It is impossible to lay down any hard-and-fast rule by which the work of horses at different ages should be governed, but the following scale may be accepted as a fair average allowance for the season:--

Age	Number of Mares
2 years old	10 to 15
3 years old	25 to 30
4 years old	45 to 60
5 years old and upwards	70 to 100

In some circumstances barrenness in a mare is largely attributable to reproductive failure of the stallion servicing her. It is too much the fashion to regard the mare as the ever-erring partner, and to overlook the disability of the horse to render his services fruitful; but how often is it observed that numbers of mares both old and young which have been regular breeders fail in a particular season to a particular horse to bear foals.

This is an occurrence so common as to be within the knowledge of everyone concerned with horse-breeding or stud management.

Explanations of various kinds are always forthcoming to account for these stud failures, some implicating the mares and others the season, but the shrewd breeder, while allowing for the possible adverse influence of both these causes, does not fail to recognize that other and more potent factor, the sire.

How much of this failure is due to impotence on his part cannot be precisely stated, but there can be no doubt that under the circumstances presently to be referred to it is the predominating quantity. When we consider the exhausting services which stud-horses have to render during the season, and the indifferent preparation many of them undergo in anticipation of the work before them, it is not surprising that they sometimes fail to give the results expected of them.

Should any suspicions arise as to the fertility of the stallion a semen evaluation should be asked of a competent veterinarian.

The practice of turning a horse away into a loose-box after the season is over, to spend the winter in confinement, and too frequently on poor feed, is, even in these enlightened days, of common occurrence, and often is the foundation on which subsequent failure of the stud is laid.

When to this is added the obesity into which he is rapidly brought during a few weeks of forcing treatment in the spring, little then remains to be done to defeat the object for which he is intended. It is not suggested that fat horses are necessarily impotent, but that they fail to meet the full and legitimate requirements of those who use them, and pay for a fruitful service. In saying so, we recognize the fact that, in order to command a liberal stud fee, sires often must be brought up to show standard, and at a time too when they should be in 'racing trim'.

In this connection it must be admitted that the users are not altogether free from blame for the losses which they suffer, and until they can judge 'make and shape', and select their sires in the absense of soft superfluous flesh and fat, owners of stallions will continue the abuse to which we have referred.

When a horse commences his season in an overly fat condition, his stud work is greatly multiplied by mares returning to service, and especially if--as is mostly the case--he is allowed to serve an unreasonable number. In this state his early services are often abortive, and require to be repeated again and again, so that the vigor and condition with which he should have started is never attained. Young and old horses especially are made to suffer, both in body and reputation, by neglect of this first principle of stud-management.

Stallions which have passed through an average season show the effects of its weakening influence, and need at that time as much as any a liberal measure of support. To uphold condition is the end to be aimed at, if a high state of fertility is to be maintained and services prolonged.

In order that this may be done, the winter keep should be generous and of the best. A paddock with ample range, if

possible should be provided, in which exercise and plenty of
it may be obtained. Stallions are better in the open, even in
the cold days of winter, than in the average stable.

As February comes round, the food ration should be increased, and exercise should be enforced. Hard condition and
a fruitful season will be the result, to say nothing of the escape from diseases incidental to obesity.

With judicious management, horses exercised will uphold
their condition as the season goes on, and far exceed in fruit-
fulness those that 'stand' at home. How much the vitality
and strength of the offspring depend upon the vigor of the
sire at the time of service is an unknown quantity, but no one
acquainted with the subject will fail to realize the importance
of their physiological relations.

It is distinctly to the advantage of stud-horses that they
be regularly fed, and ample time be allowed for digestion to
advance, before going to service. Neglect of this precaution
is accountable for many of those attacks of indigestion,
twisted bowels, and ruptured stomach from which stallions
so frequently suffer. Nor is it less important that, as far as
practicable, breeding stallions should do their work in the
early morning and cool of the evening, so that the depressing
effects of mid-day heat may be avoided.

REPRODUCTION

The one prominent function of the reproductive system
is the perpetuation of the race, and using the term in its
widest sense, reproduction includes all the processes which
result in the multiplication of living beings.

Reference to the description of the organs which constitute the reproductive system in the higher animals--the
mammals, for example--will show that two sets of complicated structure belonging to two sexes--male and female--
are concerned in the function, and a knowledge of the functions of the two distinct sets of organs will leave no room for
doubt that the female has the largest share in the perpetuation
of the species. The ovum of the female animal or plant contains all the material necessary for the formation of a new
animal or plant. In the ovum or egg there is a dormant

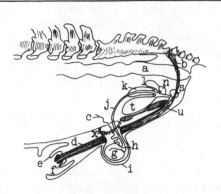

The reproductive system of the stallion: a) rectum, b) retractor penis muscle, c) spermatic vessels, d) penis, e) fold of the internal prepuce, f) free part of the penis, g) testicle, h) epididymus, i) scrotum, j) vas deferens, k) ampulla, l) seminal vessicle n) prostate, s) Cowper's gland, u) urethra, and x) inguinal ring.

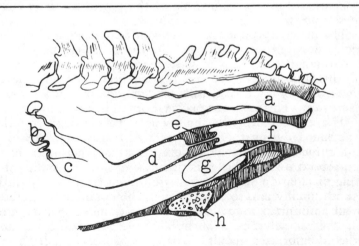

The reproductive system of the mare: a) rectum, b) ovary, c) uterine horn, d) uterus body, e) cervix, f) vagina, g) bladder, and h) mammary gland.

vitality, which only awaits contact with the sperm-cell of the male to become actively alive and capable of appropriating the material by which it is surrounded, and developing into all the tissues and organs which constitute the new existence.

The female reproduction anatomy is illustrated in the diagram below. As illustrated, the ovaries are not located within the uterine tube, but just outside the end of it. The uterine tube is somewhat funnel shaped with many small finger-like projections called fimbria. The cells that line the uterine tube have tiny cilia and secrete mucous. The beating of the cilia, which are microscopic hair-like projections, creates a current of mucous, which is evidently responsible for moving the ovum into the tube. The end of the tube usually partially surrounds the ovary so that this process is facilitated.

The uterine tubes each empty into a horn of the uterus. In the mare, the body of the uterus is quite large in comparison to the horns. The neck of the uterus is the cervix. It is actually an extremely long sphincter muscle, which remains tightly closed, sealed with a mucous plug, except during heat or at parturition. The opening of the cervix can be viewed with the use of a vaginal speculum.

The male reproductive system is also diagramed. The testicles are located outside of the body cavity, permitting spermatozoa to develop in a temperature somewhat lower than the internal temperature of the body. Often one or both testicles fail to descend from the abdominal cavity into the scrotum. This is known as cryptorchidism.

The epididymus acts mainly as a storage depot for the spermatozoa during the final stages of maturation. It takes about three weeks for completely mature spermatozoa to form. About one third of this time is spent in the epididymus. During ejaculation spermatozoa are drawn from the epididymus and quickly pass to the exterior. The epididymus secretes a small amount of mucous which helps to move spermatozoa along the vas deferens. The bulk of the ejaculate is secreted by the accessory sex glands.

The ampulla is an enlargement of the vas deferens which contain glandular cells. These add a small amount of secretion to the spermatozoa. The seminal vesicles (paired) secrete the albumen portion of the semen, which greatly increases the bulk of the ejaculate. The prostate gland produces a milky secretion as the last portion of the ejaculate. It is located at the junction of the two vas deferens and the urethra. The Cowper's gland produces a thin grayish fluid, which is the first portion of the semen to come out.

With the impregnation of the germ-cell by the action of the male, the more complicated function of the female begins, and must go on until the new creature is sufficiently advanced to live an independent existance. A merely superficial analysis of the function thus lightly sketched, reveals the three essentials of which it consists, namely, impregnation, gestation, and parturation, each of which includes certain conditions which vary in different beings.

IMPREGNATION

Successful horse-breeding demands a special knowledge of horses, so far as concerns their external conformation, aptitudes for different services, and peculiarities and defects; and in its practical aspect it requires also a sound knowledge of horse-rearing and management, particularly of the young stock, and of mares during pregnancy and parturition, and for some time after that event. Constant care and attention are likewise needed on the part of those entrusted with the carrying out of the details of breeding, in order to avoid accidents and ensure a satisfactory result.

The age at which horses commence to breed depends to some extent upon breed peculiarities and external conditions, which have an influence in promoting precocity or retarding puberty. Well-bred animals are more precocious in this direction than those which are under-bred, and an abundance of rich stimulating food, easy labor and comfortable surroundings expedite the development of the procreative faculties. The male and female horse are capable of breeding at two years of age, but instances are on record in which yearling colts and fillies have copulated successfully, and foals have been born before the parents were two years old.

The duration of the period during which procreation is possible is also dependent upon circumstances connected with breed, management, and surroundings. The stallion may continue potent until over thirty years of age, and mares have been known to produce foals when twenty-eight, thirty-two, and thirty-eight years old. But it may be accepted as a rule stallions and mares are at their best from four or five years, until they are about sixteen years old.

The mare is usually "in season" (ready to receive the stallion) from April to June, or even later, and the periods when conception is likely to take place during that time recur about every three weeks, and are very brief in some mares-- only of two or three day's duration. The indications of this condition (estrum) are generally well marked: the animal is usually irritable or sluggish, and less able to sustain severe

The stallion may continue potent until over 30 years of age.

exertion; the sensibility is increased, and the appetite is more or less in abeyance or capricious, and thirst is often present; there is a tendency to seek the company of other horses, especially males; attempts to pass urine are frequent, and there are spasmodic ejections of a whitish fluid, accompanied by movements of the vulva. While these symptoms continue, the mare will readily receive "service", and fecundation then most certainly occurs,--though it must be remarked that they often persist continuously in certain mares, and "service" does not allay them, neither does pregnancy result from such service, as they are mostly due to an abnormal condition of the ovaries.

When conception has taken place, these symptoms, as a rule, do not recur at these usual periods, and are not witnessed during the whole time of pregnancy,--though now and again instances are noted in which one or more of them are observed, and pregnant mares will sometimes accept the stallion, instead of repelling him, as is usually the case, though he rarely shows any desire to have intercourse with mares when they are in foal.

When conception has taken place, the signs of heat or rutting, as has been said, subside, and are not again noticed until after parturition; they reappear, however, very soon after that act has taken place, and it is believed that on the ninth day subsequent to foaling, the mare will be more successfully impregnated than at any other time.

With some mares impregnation does not take place readily, and this fault may be due to various causes, such as the animal being too old when tried for the first time, too fat or debilitated, etc., in which cases medicines which stimulate the reproductive functions may be of service. For other cases in which the cause is located in the organs of reproduction, the remedy to be resorted to will depend upon the character of the obstacle. The most frequent of the causes which hinder or prevent impregnation and produce sterility appears to be one of a mechanical kind--closure of the small opening (os) in the neck (cervix) of the uterus, leading to the interior of that important receptacle. This can only be ascertained by a manual examination, which discovers the opening into the uterus to be impervious, through contraction or alteration in structure of the neck of that organ. For very many of those cases the canal can be dilated by the fingers, covered with a sterile glove, immediately before the mare is brought to the stallion.

When impregnation has been successfully accomplished, certain changes are often observed in the behavior of the mare. Perhaps the most notable indication is the disappearance of "estrum" or "heat". It is ordinarily the practice to present a mare to the stallion nine days after she has foaled, during what is known as the "foal heat". About three weeks afterwards she is again presented, and generally in another three weeks a last trial is made. At this time, if the animal refuses the stallion it is concluded that she is settled, especially if she has not shown signs of "heat" in the intervening time.

PREGNANCY

In a short time after impregnation the majority of mares become quieter and more docile and may begin to put on some fat. Seldom is anything more noticed, externally, until pregnancy has advanced to the sixth or seventh month. Because of this it is the general procedure to have a veterinarian check the mare for pregnancy about thirty to forty-five days after conception.

There are several techniques used by veterinarians for pregnancy diagnosis. By far the most common is rectal palpation. The arm is covered with a rubber or plastic glove and inserted in the rectum of the mare. As the uterus lies directly below the rectum and the ovaries to each side, it is quite easy

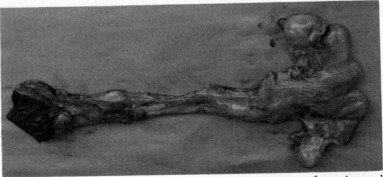

A dissected mare uterus shows the normal position of ovaries and uterine horns below the rectum.

to palpate the genital system, if the mare is sufficiently re-laxed. The bulge in the pregnant uterine horn is no bigger than a walnut, at 30 days, and may be difficult to detect without considerable experience. The bulge enlarges three to four times within the next week. It is the size of an orange at about forty days, and a football at two months.

A relatively simple blood test has been developed which can detect pregnancy from about the fortieth day up to about the one hundred and thirtieth day. It is quite accurate and is very useful for routine checking of large numbers of mares. It is known as the hemagglutination—inhibition test, which checks for the gonadotropin hormone in pregnant mare serum.

But about the sixth or seventh month an attentive ob-server can generally detect an enlargement of the abdomen, more particularly on the right side, and movements of the young creature can also be seen in the region of the right flank, and most probably after the mare has been drinking cold water. The expert may also be able to hear the beating of the fetal heart.

From this time onwards the size of the abdomen gradually increases, and it becomes more pendulous and prominent, though the volume varies in different mares, the variation de-pending not only upon a difference in the size of the foal, but also upon the amount of the fluid which surrounds it in the uterus, this being much greater in some mares than others.

When the term of pregnancy is nearly completed, not only is the abdomen increasingly larger and more pendulous, but its upper part on both sides towards the spine begins to fall in, this hollowness being very marked immediately before parturition. A waxy matter also forms on the teats, and the udder becomes enlarged, this enlargement being generally coincident with the appearance of a thin discharge from the teats. The mare becomes sluggish, is readily tired, and seeks for rest and tranquillity, though the appetite, which has been greater during the later months of pregnancy than before, is usually unimpaired. A few days before foaling the croup sinks on each side of the root of the tail, and sometimes the hind-limbs swell slightly.

V. GESTATION

Impregnation is effected by the contact of the sperm-cell of the male with the germ-cell of the female. The precise manner of the contact, and the means employed to ensure it, are of no consequence to the result. In the most highly organized mammals, for instance, the fluid secreted by the testicles of the male (semen), with fluid from the prostate and other glands, is conveyed to the reproductive organs of the female by means of the intromittent organ, which injects it forcibly into the vagina, and to some extent also through the open mouth of the uterus into that organ. Sperm-cells, or, as they may more correctly be termed, spermatozoa, which have been set free from the sperm-cells, are abundant in the fluid so injected. These actively moving bodies are the essential agents in impregnation, and whether they reach the germ-cells of the ovum in the natural way, or are conveyed artifically by instrumental means, as in artifical insemination, the effect of their contact is the same. The previously passive germ-cell becomes active under the stimulus imparted by the sperm-cell, which rouses the developmental force of the ovum.

Another important factor in the reproductive function is the receptive condition of the ovum. Not every contact between the sperm and the germ is fruitful. The ova in the ovarium are not at all times ready to react to the mysterious force which the sperm-cell is ready to transmit.

During the period of life which includes the power of procreation, development of ova is always going on in the substance of the ovary. From a mere speck of germinal matter or protoplasm, the egg originates as a simple cell, gradually attaining to the condition of the mature ovum with its external vitelline membrane (zona pellucida), the yolk-sac containing the yolk and a germinal vesicle with the central germinal spot. As the development of the ovum reaches

61

nearer to the point of perfection, the Graafian follicle in which it is contained and protected, advances to the surface of the ovarium, blood circulation in the external membranes increases in volume and rapidity, and soon the surface of the Graafian follicle is covered with an arboresque arrangement of brightly colored vessels. In due time the follicle bursts and sets the mature ovum free to pass into the open fimbriated mouth of the Fallopian tube, through which it passes to the interior of the uterus. If no contact takes place with the sperm-cell, the ovum, although ready to receive the stimulus, which, however, may not be present, passes into the uterus and forms part of the waste products of the mucous membrane, and with them is expelled, one of the many instances of the reckless liberality of the natural functions, which are constantly supplying redudant matter for the development of new organs or repair of wasted tissue-matter which is often in excess of the demand, or is supplied unconsciously when the conditions are not favorable to its fruitful use.

Changes in the mammalian ovum during its progress to maturity are continually occurring, from the time of puberty to the end of the productive life of the animal. Its mature state is reached with the occurrence of estrum or heat, and it is to be noticed that during the few days of continuance of this condition there is a marked increase of sexual excitement. The mature ovum or ova are at this time discharged from the Graafian follicle.

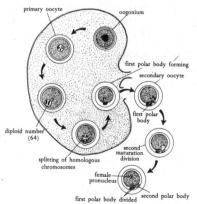

Maturation of the ovum.

An idea of the form and structure of the mammalian ovum may be gained from an examination of the egg of a bird. The common fowl furnishes the most simple examples, simple because they are prominent objects, easily seen by the unaided eye, while the mammalian ovum is a microscopic object, only to be distinguished by the aid of a highly magnifying power.

In the above illustration a diagram, with description, exhibits the ovum lying in the Graafian vesicle. From its origin to its maturation the chief changes which occur in the ovum are those incidental to its growth, and the necessary advance of the body from the centre of the Graffian vesicle to its circumference. The germinal vesicle itself, as maturity in the ovum advances, becomes relatively smaller, owing to the more rapid growth of the structures with which it is associated.

While the ovum is advancing to the circumference of the Graafian vesicle, the granular contents of that vesicle are pushed to the inner side of the investing membrane which forms its wall, and becomes the *membrana granulosa,* in which the ovum itself is embedded.

To continue the story, it must be granted that one or more of several mature ova meet the sperm-cells, which can start their dormant life into activity, and in such case on the instant of contact commence the changes which end in the formation of a miniature representation of the parent.

At what stage of its progress from the ovary through the Fallopian tubes to the cavity of the uterus the ovum meets the sperm-cell from the seminal fluid is not known. The spermatozoa are capable of rapid movements, and may meet the advancing ovum at any point of its course, even from the moment of its exit from the ovary. Wherever the contact between the germ-cell and the sperm-cell occurs, the resulting changes are wonderful and also inexplicable. First it is evident that active developmental powers exert themselves, and effect in the contents of the ovum remarkable structural changes.

After the disappearance of the germinal vesicle, curious changes in the yolk are perceived, resulting in segmentation. First, depressions or notches are noticed in the membrane surrounding the yolk at two points, and these slowly advance through the mass, cutting it in halves, while almost at the same time a similar process is going on in each half, making four divisions, which are divided again and again, until a mulberry mass if formed.

Completion of the process of segmentation leaves the yolk a mass of delicate granular spherical masses, each with a clear center. Conversion of these masses into cells is effected by the development of an investing membrane round each mass. As soon as the cell-formation is perfected, the peripheral cells arrange themselves on the surface of the yolk, the central masses follow, and finally complete the construction of a thick membrane, which soon divides into two layers, and development of the embryo begins in earnest.

DEVELOPMENT OF THE EMBRYO

The attempt to describe the formation of the various parts of the young animal is difficult because by no form of verbal gymnastics is it possible to describe a whole set of simultaneous processes by the aid of consecutive phrases. It is easy, for example, to state the fact that in the germinal membrane the embryo is formed; that bones, muscles, integument, and viscera appear, and that adaptive changes go on in the uterus, in which the young one has to pass its embryonic and fetal life; but unless the reader will consent to make a mental effort to realize that the changes are all going on in different degrees at the same time, there is no hope that the writer will succeed in conveying a correct idea of the true nature of the developmental process.

Proceeding from the point which has just been reached, the formation of a germinal membrane by an accumulation of cells round the inside of the investing membrane of the yolk (yolk-sac), it will be quite easy to understand that at a certain part in the blastodermic membrane a round mass of cells appears, called for the sake of distinction the ger-

minal area. In this round mass, which soon becomes an oval
mass, the first sign of the embryo is seen, as shown in the
accompanying figure.

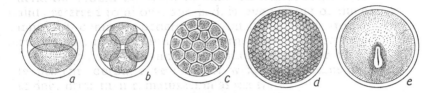

The development of the ovum
a. First division of the ovum; b, c, d, subdivision of the ovum; e. first trace of the
embryo.

On each side the primitive groove or trace above described, are collected two oval masses of cells rising above
the plane of the germinal membrane and bending towards
each other until they touch and form an arch in which
the incipient spinal cord is to be lodged; all this is arranged,
it must be observed, in the upper or serous layer of the germinal membrane. Immediately below the primitive groove
a line of cells may be recognized, forming the *chorda dorsalis,*
the rudimentary stage of the bodies of the bones of the back
(dorsal vertebrae). Then below the primitive groove, at the
same time that the cells of the laminae dorsalis are closing
over to form the central canal for the spinal cord, the serous
membrane sends off prolongations from its lower margin, the
laminae ventrales, which unite to form the walls of the trunk
to enclose the abdominal viscera.

As they proceed downwards, the *ventral laminae* turn
inwards, enclosing part of the yolk-sac, after which the yolk
and inner muscous layer of the germinal membrane are divided into two portions, one being retained in the body of
the embryo, the other being left outside. The latter is called
the umbilical vesicle. The mucous layer of the germinal
membrane now lines the interior of the abdominal cavity
and also the interior of the umbilical vesicle. The upper or
serous layer is continued round both, and from the portion of

the muscous layer enclosed in the body of the embryo the intestinal canal is developed.

This state of the embryo is represented in the next illustration.

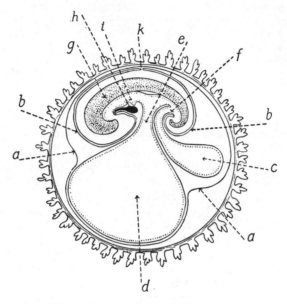

Development of the embryo, eighteenth day.
a. Outer or corneous layer; b. amnion; c. allantois connected with the anal portion of the alimentary canal; d. yolksac or umbilical vesicle; e. vitello-intestinal opening; f. simple alimentary canal in lower position; g. trunk and head of embryo; h. fetal heart; i. alimentary canal in upper portion; k. place of convergence of amnion and reflexion of false amnion or corneous layer.

While the changes above described have been going on, the formation of the fetal membranes, the allantois and amnion, is proceeding. Folds of the external layer of the blastodermic membrane are raised to enclosed the body of the embryo forming the amnion; at the same time during the development of the amnion the allantois protrudes from the hinder portion of the intestinal canal, as a small pear-shaped mass of cells at first, but, rapidly extending, it presses its way between the folds of the amnion and comes in close contact with the outer one of the two folds, becoming more vascular as it proceeds. Reaching the umbilicus, the allantois is divided into two parts. The outer part, however, extending to the external investure of the ovum, the chorion, shrivels, and is lost; the other portion remains in the abdominal cavity, and part of it is converted into the urinary bladder, while the remaining portion extends from the bladder to the umbilicus under the name of arachus which after birth forms one of the ligaments of the bladder.

The accompanying figure shows the arrangement of the three membranes which invest the ovum, i.e. the external chorion, the amnion, the outer portion of which becomes in part firmly attached to the inside of the chorion, and the allantoid sac.

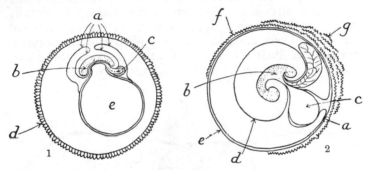

Development of the human ovum.

1. Early stage: a. interior and exterior folds of the serous layer joining the amnion; b. embryo; c. incipient allantois; d. chorion; e. vitelline mass surrounded by blastodermic vesicle. 2. Second month: a. amnion, outer layer, coalescing with chorion; b. embryo; c. umbilical vesicle; d. amnion, inner layer; e. smooth portion of chorion; f. villous portion of chorion; g. elongated villi collecting into placenta.

The villi on the outer surface of the chorion of the human ovum are seen to be massed on the right side of the figure shown to form the placenta. In the equine ovum there is no circumscribed placenta, but instead the vascular villi are connected throughout with the internal uterine membrane by means of numerous placental tufts, which penetrate the lining of the uterus so that the capillaries of the fetal vessels and those of the maternal vessels are in contact over the whole surface. There is, however, no actual communication between the two sets of capillaries, but the bloodstream of the mother and that of the fetus are separated only by the thin walls of the vessels, through which the blood is constantly flowing. The interchange which takes place between the maternal and the fetal blood, for the nutrition of the young animal, necessarily is carried on through the two layers of membrane by osmosis, i.e. that force which regulates the interchange of fluids through wet membrane.

Blood-vessels in the embryo commence by formation of a thin membrane in the blastoderm, between the serous and mucous layers, at a part which is described as the vascular area. Red lines appear, and form a network of vessels filled with blood, a rudimentary heart is formed in the vascular area, and to that organ the branching vessels proceed, and the outline of the circulatory system is complete; the details being filled in by further developments in correspondence with the continuous advance of the embryonic structures.

In the next illustration the condition of the embryo and its membrance at the age of seven weeks is shown.

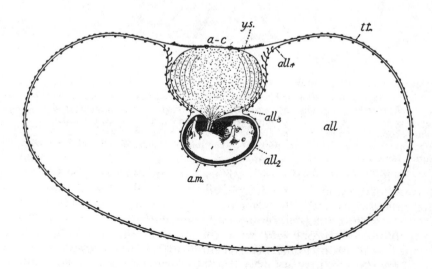

Embryo of horse at seven weeks

UTERINE CHANGES IN GESTATION

Further consideration of embroyonic growth and development may be deferred in order to explain the adaptive alterations which have up to this time taken place in the uterus.

At an early period in utero-gestation the openings of the mucous membrane lining the uterus increase in size and become more numerous. Meanwhile the membrane itself receives additions which render it softer, thicker, and more vascular than the normal membrane; in fact, the added materials constitute a new membrane under the name of the *membrana decidua*, which is afterwards divided into three layers-the decidua *vera*, decidua *reflexa*, and decidua *serotina*; the last named is especially devoted to the reception of the villi of the chorion. In the cavity of the uterus a quantity of fluid rich in nucleated cells collects, in contact with the deciduous membrane and the chorion, aiding in the process of nutrition and purification of the fetal blood.

The membranes which have been described as surrounding the embryo also contain fluid, and the young animal during the whole of its existence in the uterus is surrounded and protected by water cushions of the most perfect construction.

It may be mentioned incidentally that all the membranes belonging to the fetus, with a large portion of the deciduous linings of the uterus, are cast off at the time of parturition as the after-birth, and the uterine mucous membrane gradually returns to its former condition.

DEVELOPMENT OF THE ORGANS

Up to this point the object of the writer has been to convey to the reader some idea of the very interesting subject of embryonic development from the mature ovum, which is a mere speck about the one one-thousandths of an inch in diameter, to the point at which the rudiments of the young animal are formed, and the embryo is in vascular connection with the mother by the contact of the vessels of the chorion surrounding the ovum with those of the lining membrane of the uterus, so arranged that nutriment may be transferred from the parent to the offspring, and the otygenation of the blood be effected by the process of osmosis. Thus the placental union may be looked upon as representing an organ of respiration as well as of nutrition.

Growth and development continue from the stage at which the embryo was left at the seventh week to the period when the embryo becomes the fetus, about the fourth month all the organs then being miniature representations of those of the animal when separated from the mother by the act of parturition.

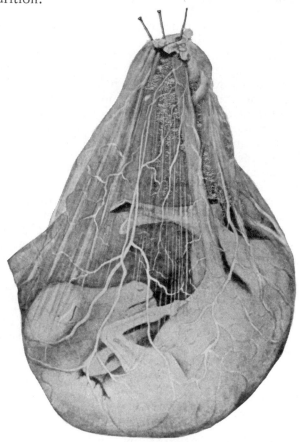

Foal about Fourth Month

An account of the further steps in the development of the embryo is shown in the accompanying table (from Mares, Foals and Foaling by Friedrich Andrist).

WEIGHT AND DIMENSIONS OF UNBORN FOAL

End of Month	Length Poll to root of dock	Weight	Stage of development
1	1¼ in.	minute	All internal organs present
2	3–3¾ in.	minute	Limbs distinct. Sex recognizable. There is about 1 oz. of fluid inside the membranes
3	5 in.	4½–6 oz.	The villi or tufts of the outer membrane are forming, and so are the hoofs. Ends of cannon bones ossifying
4	8–9 in.	2 lb.	Some fluids present in foetal stomach. First traces of hair round lips. Union between maternal and foetal systems complete
5	8–9 in.	4 lb. 4 oz.	Traces of hair above eyes and on tip of tail. External sexual organs formed
6	22 in.	12 lb. 12 oz.	Hair much more apparent
7	23–25 in.	29¾–34 lb.	Mane growing
8	27–29 in.	36–42 lb.	Hair all along spine
9	30–33 in.	51–57 lb.	Short hairs all over body. Might just survive if born now
10	34–37 in.	64–74 lb.	Coat and long hairs fully grown
11	43 in. and upwards	85–107 lb.	Milk molars through gums. Sometimes nippers also

In the early embryo the formation of the line of cells below the primitive trace was described as the *chorda dorsalis*, the basis of the future backbone or vertebral column. Conversion of the gelatinous mass of cells into bone is the simple result of the deposition of bone-earth, calcium phosphate and carbonate mainly. With the ossification is associated the necessary elaboration of form of the bones, ending in the development of the bodies, arches, and processes of the vertebral bones, which are divisible into neck, back, loins, and tail--i.e. cervical, dorsal, lumbar, sacral, and coccygeal bones. At the anterior part of the vertebral column a prolongation of the structures occurs, to form the cranium to contain the brain, and next the bones of the face are formed from a series of arches derived from the visceral lamina, which have been described.

The four limbs or extremities at the same time are growing from the lamina which form the boundaries of the trunk, and it is noticeable that in all vertebrate animals the four extremities are at first identical in form, whether their ultimate use is to be for walking, grasping, swimming, or flying; in other words, whether the extremities are to be finally feet or hands, or fins or wings, they all have the same shape at first. The highest mammal in the course of embryonic development exhibits some of the features of the reptile, fish, and bird, a good example of evolution in a compressed form never exciting any astonishment, because it is never seen by the ordinary eye, being hidden in the membranes which invest the ovum, and only to be detected by elaborate and minute dissection by a practiced anatomist skilled in the use of the most delicate instruments.

In its primitive condition the heart is a mass of cells to which, as already described in the embryo, the vessels of the vascular area tend and ultimately reach, forming the rudiments of the circulatory system.

Cavities are constructed in the mass of cells representing the heart, which become separated to form the ventricles and auricles. Blood vessels which were formerly only red lines acquire size and shape, and divide themselves into arteries and veins, and gradually the complicated mechanism of circulation is elaborated from a few clusters of cells.

Long before birth the fetus possesses a perfectly complete set of organs connected with the circulation, differing in a few details of construction to meet the peculiarities of the fetal environment. To understand the circulation of the blood in the unborn foal, it is desirable to refer to the description of the circulation of the blood in the adult horse.

In regard to the fetal circulation, it will be convenient to commence with the umbilical arteries, two in number, which convey the blood which has already passed over the body of the fetus to the vascular tufts which constitute the placenta. The blood so conveyed effects an exchange of its effete matters through the walls of the fetal and the maternal capillaries, and receives in return nutriment and oxygen. Thus renovated, the blood is carried back by the converging capillaries, which unite to form the umbilical vein, which vessel with the two umbilical arteries and the urachus mainly constitute the umbilical cord. The blood in the umbilical arteries is really in the fetus comparable to the venous blood in the mature animal, while the umbilical vein receives the renovated blood, and thus performs the function of an artery.

Passing through the navel (*umbilicus*), the vein enters the liver of the fetus, and in the horse pours the whole of its blood into the portal vein. In animals other than soliped or single-hoofed, the vein divides before entering the liver, and sends part of its blood directly through a separate branch (the *ductus venosus*) into the posterior vena cava. In the equine fetus, however, all the blood gets into the vena cava at last, and thence to the right auricle of the heart, which cavity also receives the blood from the anterior part of the body through the anterior vena cava. This blood goes directly through the auricle into the right ventricle, while the blood from the posterior vena cava is directed by the Eustachian valve through an opening (the *foramen ovale*) in the muscular wall which divides the right from the left auricle, and at once passes to the left ventricle, and by the contraction of the walls of that cavity is driven over the body after having met with the blood in the right ventricle, which has passed into the pulmonary artery in the ordinary course, but instead of reaching the lungs has been diverted into the arterial duct (*ductus arteriosus*), which in the fetus leads directly from the pulmonary artery to the posterior aorta. It is of course understood that the fetal lungs are not respiratory organs, as no air can reach them; therefore nothing would be gained by the blood entering them in large quantity; in fact, that fluid has been aerated in passing through the placenta. After circulating over the body, the blood is again carried by the pulmonary arteries to the placenta, and the course of the circulation just described is repeated. The total result of the modification in the arrangement of the circulatory apparatus in the fetus is the distribution of mixed blood over the body; only that portion which passes through the umbilical arteries reaches the placenta and becomes oxidized and otherwise improved by the interchanges which take place between the maternal and fetal fluids.

As soon as the structures forming the body boundaries of the spinal column and cranium are ready for their recepttion, the spinal cord and the brain are formed, constituting the cerebro-spinal system; the eyes, organs of hearing and taste, are gradually developed by the ordinary processes of cell formation.

The alimentary canal has already been referred to in connection with the mucous layer of the blastodermic membrane, and it may be observed that from the same source the other organs of the abdominal cavity, and also the organs of respiration, are formed, and the fetal structures are, so far as general outline is concerned, complete. The subsequent processes are those of growth due to the continually added supplies of nutriment, until the young animal is fit for "separate life", when various influences act upon the uterus and cause explusion of the fetus in the act of parturition.

For some time, however, the foal has to depend on its mother for its subsistence, and as soon as it can rise to the erect position, instinctively it seeks for the teats of the dam, from which for some months to come it will obtain its chief food.

By degrees the foal, prompted by instinct or curiosity, essays the taste of the herbage at its feet, and in time begins to perfer it to the maternal fluid. The mother at the same time seems to realize that her nursing days have been sufficiently prolonged, and gives her colt emphatic hints that it has ceased to be solely dependent on her for its daily food.

CARE OF THE MARE DURING GESTATION

During the early months of pregnancy the mare demands no special care beyond that included in the term "good stable management". But towards the sixth month she should be more carefully treated than she would be if not in foal. If she is ridden rather extensively then it ought to be, if possible not so rapid, and be gentler and more uniform—violent paces or irregular and severe efforts are attended with danger, all the more imminent as pregnancy is advanced, and particularly so towards its finish. Within a week or two of foaling all work should cease, but exercise ought to be allowed if the mare is not in a paddock, though with care mares may be ridden lightly until within a few days of foaling. It must be remembered that exercise is beneficial, and indeed necessary, for all breeds of mares during pregnancy; but if they are allowed to run out-of-doors this should be on as level ground as possible, with a soil in which the feet will not sink, and without ditches or holes.

Mares when in foal, and especially when near foaling time, have a greater tendency to indulge in rolling than at other times when lying down, and if there are hollows, open drains, or ditches, they may become fixed in one of these, and in their struggles to get up so strain themselves as to make parturition difficult, or lead to abortion or death of the foal. All the walls or fences enclosing the fields or paddocks in which pregnant mares are kept should have no gaps or stakes projecting inwards, and all doors and gates through which such animals may have to pass ought to be sufficiently wide to permit them to pass through quite easily. Pregnant mares should not be pastured with young horses or cattle, nor exposed to anything likely to cause excitement.

The same care ought to be observed if the mare is stabled. She must be protected from annoyance or injury by other horses, and if kept in a stall this ought to be of ample width, to allow her to turn round easily in it. The floor should also be as level and horizontal as possible, so that the mare may stand and lie easily, and the weight of the abdominal contents not be thrown too much backwards. The mare should also be fastened by the head in such a manner that there may be no danger of her getting cast.

But it is always judicious to have a mare about to foal kept in a convenient loose-box or temporary shed, where there is plenty of room for her to move about, with protection from inclement weather, freedom from draughts of cold air, and good ventilation.

For litter, straw is suitable, though when parturition is near this should not be new, as some mares have a kind of morbid appetite at this time and would consume it greedily, thereby producing abdominal distention and consequently dangerous pressure on the uterus and its contents. Long new straw also becomes twisted and rolled round the feet, and so impedes movement. It is therefore advisable to use slightly soiled but dry litter that has been under other horses--this is soft and broken, so that the mare's feet will not become entangled in it, and being soiled she will not eat it.

With regard to food, the kind and quantity allowed will depend upon the state of pregnancy which the mare has reached. If she is exercised, the quantity and quality should be sufficient to maintain her in good health and efficient condition--if anything it ought to be better in quality and a little more in quantity than that given to similar-sized horses not in foal, and it should, if possible, be presented more frequently. Whether the mare is or is not ridden, it is advisable not to allow her to become fat--indeed it is preferable to keep her in what might be termed moderate condition. Good hay and oats is generally adequate feed for pregnant mares. In areas of deficiency soils, vitamin and mineral supplements may need to be added to the diet. Dusty and moldy feed should be avoided. Good alfalfa hay serves as a good feed for pregnant mares.

Many mares at pasture receive nothing but the grass they pick up, and when there is plenty of this and it is of good quality, the mare may do well and produce a well-developed foal; but during unfavorable weather, or when the the pasturage is scanty or poor, a suitable quantity of hay and oats should be allowed, especially for morning feed; indeed at all times an allowance of oats, even if small, is advantageous.

All food should not only be of good quality, but be also capable of easy digestion. A very excellent adjunct to the diet is a lump of rock-salt placed in a position where the mare can conveniently get at it to lick it.

Medicines should never be administered to pregnant mares except under skilled advice.

With regard to drink, the water should be clean and pure, and allowed frequently. If the mare is stabled it should be always beside her, as then there will be no danger of her drinking too much at a time. Soft water is better than that which is hard.

As will be seen, much of the success that should attend horse-breeding depends upon the care and attention bestowed upon the mare towards and at foaling time, as then not only are her own health and safety at stake, but the welfare of her progeny is also a matter for serious consideration. But if suitable precautions are adopted and intelligent observation maintained, the mare and foal usually pass through this critical period of their existence in a satisfactory manner. It is certainly true that in very many instances pregnant mares receive little notice beyond that given at other times, and are often hard-worked and exposed to all kinds of unfavorable treatment. But this treatment is not always pursued with impunity, for accidents of a serious kind often occur, and sometimes the foal, sometimes the mare--not infrequently both--suffer disastrously. Common-bred animals are less predisposed to accidents at this time than the purebred--high breeding bringing in its train greater liability to certain accidents incidental to pregnancy and parturition. Purebred animals therefore generally require more careful supervision on the part of the breeder.

ABORTION

Abortion and premature birth are the most serious accidents that can happen to pregnant mares. Though both terms are often applied indiscriminately, "slipping the foal" is the term generally employed when the young creature is expelled at any time before it is fully developed and the usual time of pregnancy has expired; yet it is recognized by those who make this subject their study that the term "abortion" should imply expulsion of the fetus from the mother when it has not attained sufficient development to live outside its mother's body, while "premature birth" signifies that the young creature has been born before its time, yet with all its organs sufficiently formed to enable it to live for at least some time in the external world. In the first instance it is either dead when expelled from the uterus or it dies immediately afterwards; and in the second it may be weakly and immature and succumb after a variable period, or it may continue to live and eventually thrive. In practice, however, there is no accurately defined limit between abortion and premature birth, and especially when the latter has been brought about by any one of the causes that produce the former.

Abortion is said to take place in mares when the fetus is expelled forty days before the usual period of pregnancy has terminated, and though it may occur at any time during pregnancy, especially before the three hundredth day, yet it is much more frequent during the first than the second half of pregnancy. When the accident takes place at a very early period it may not produce any appreciable disturbance in the mare's health, and the developing ovum usually escapes intact and often unperceived; but when it occurs at a later stage it is serious, as it not only entails the loss of the foal, but may also compromise the health, or even the life, of the parent.

Many causes operate in bringing about abortion, and some of these have been mentioned; they act more or less in a mechanical manner, and usually only one mare in a number will abort. But when several cases follow each other quickly in a breeding establishment, and no sufficient reason can be assigned for their occurrence, then the question of infection arises. When, therefore, two or three abortions happen in a stud, it is well to notify a veterinarian at once.

As a preventive of infectious abortion, the surroundings of the pregnant mare should be as clean as possible, and all decaying or putrid animal or vegetable matter ought to be kept away from her. Cleanliness, good food, and pure air and water are the only efficient protectives that can be recommended against abortion, beyond those already mentioned.

When a mare shows signs of impending abortion, if she is not already housed and by herself, the first thing to be done is to remove her to a spacious loose-box, which ought to be kept rather dark, and free from noise. These signs, however, are not very obvious in all cases. Sometimes it happens that the mare appears to be as lively and well as usual up to the moment when the fetus is expelled, while the expulsive act itself is so sudden and quick, and accomplished with so little visible effort or disturbance, that the accident excites

very little if any notice. It frequently happens during the
night, and surprise is expressed at finding in the morning the
aborted fetus, usually contained in its intact envelopes, lying
behind an animal which on the previous evening looked perfectly well, and even now is so cheerful and unaltered, and its
functions so little impaired, that it can scarcely be believed
she has been the subject of such a grave mishap. Even the
sentiment of maternity, which is so strongly developed in
animals after carrying the young full time, is not awakened
in her, and she shows the utmost indifference to the fetus,
even stepping on it.

When abortion takes place during the day, the flanks
have been observed to fall in a little, the abdomen descends,
the vulva and vagina slightly dilate, and there escapes from
them a glutinous, reddish-tinged fluid, followed by the fetus.
If abortion occurs at an early period in pregnancy, the membranes in which the young creature is enclosed are not ruptured; but when the period is more advanced--it may be towards the seventh or eighth month--these envelopes rupture
before expulsion of the fetus, and may be retained in the
uterus or ejected soon afterwards.

In other instances, however, especially when pregnancy
is well advanced, and particularly if the mare has sustained
external injury, there are precursory signs of abortion which
the attentive observer may note, but which vary to some extent, according as the fetus is dead or alive. The mare suddenly appears dull and dejected, or is restless, uneasy, and
constantly moving about. If the fetus is alive and strong its
movements are--by one watching the mare's abdomen--per-
ceived to be frequent, violent, and disordered, but they soon
become feeble and infrequent, and cease altogether when it
has died. The mare shows symptoms of illness, and these are
soon succeeded by those that characterize ordinary parturition, and spontaneous birth of the dead progeny takes place,
or, in rare instances, it may be necessary to remove it man-
ually.

In other instances, when the fetus is not removed from
the mare spontaneously or artifically after it has ceased to
move in the uterus, the mare regains her ordinary tranquillity,
appetite, and liveliness, and all the symptoms disappear for
one or more days, when they are again manifested, and the

fetus may be expelled without any apparent effort, or after much straining.

When it is observed that abortion is likely to occur, it is advisable to obtain professional advice as soon as possible. If the accident has already occurred, however, then, if other pregnant mares are near, they must be at once removed to a safe distance from the place, which should be cleaned and disinfected as soon as possible. Everything in the way of litter and remains of fodder, together with the fetus and its envelopes, ought to be burned, and the ground well scraped and disinfected. The hind-quarters of the mare should also be washed with a disinfectant. Until all this has been done, and some days have elapsed, the mare must not be allowed to associate with in-foal mares. It is also advisable to prohibit persons who have attended on the mare approaching these until they have at least been disinfected.

It is a wise measure to keep pregnant mares away from horses affected with infectious or contagious diseases, such as influenza and strangles, as, if they become affected they may abort, or these diseases may be transmitted to the progeny.

VI. PARTURITION

The duration of pregnancy in the mare is usually about eleven months, though it may vary between ten and twelve months, or even more. The normal duration is, however, between three hundred and thirty and three hundred and fifty days. Some foals may be born alive from the three hundredth to the three hundredth and tenth day, but this is rare.

Breed and feeding have some influence on the duration of pregnancy. In high-bred and well-fed mares it is generally shorter than in under-bred, badly-cared for, and hard-worked animals.

Description has been made of the signs which indicate that pregnancy is drawing to a close, and it is necessary that these should be noted and acted upon, so as to be prepared for the birth of the foal; and when the event is imminent, a visit should be paid to the mare frequently by night and by day.

Birth of the foal, when all things are favorable, takes place very rapidly, and in the great majority of cases the mare requires no assistance. When the labor pains come on, and she begins to strain energetically, the foal is propelled backwards, with the fore-legs leading, and the head between them. These soon appear externally, usually surrounded by the membranes and the fluid contained in them. A few more strains and the membranes are ruptured, when the foal glides gently down over the mare's hocks, if she is standing--which is generally the case--and falls softly on to the ground; the navel-string (unbilical cord) is nearly always torn through during this descent of the foal.

The mare, soon after its birth, cleans the foal by licking it all over, and when this is done it is well to offer her a bucket of grain mixed with bran, but otherwise she ought to

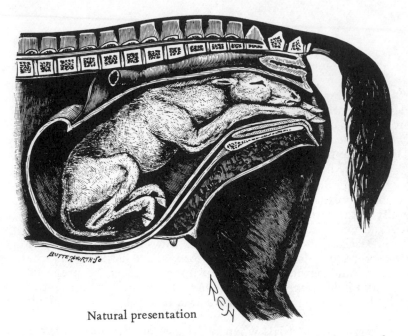

Natural presentation

be interfered with as little as possible. In some instances the mare refuses to have anything to do with the foal, and even becomes aggressive towards it. In such cases it has been recommended to sprinkle the foal's back with flour, as an inducement for the dam to lick this off, and so to become attached to her progeny.

The explusion of the membranes, or "after-birth", sometimes takes place with the birth of the foal, but it is generally subsequent to that event within a few hours. If they are retained until they begin to putrefy, serious consequences may ensue; it is necessary to remove them in a day or so. If they are apparent, or readily accessible to the hand, they may be gently twisted round like a rope and slightly pulled upon until they are brought away. If this procedure is not successful, then the hand and arm, well soaped or oiled, must be introduced into the uterus, and the membranes seized, disengaged from their attachments, and completely removed from the mare. This attempt is all the more urgently necessary when there is a foul odor from the membranes and a bad-smelling discharge from the vagina, the mare at the same time making attempts to strain, and looking feverish. Then not only must every portion of these membranes be removed from the uterine cavity, but this must be thoroughly cleansed by copious injections of warm water, to which disinfectant has been added, and scrupulous cleanliness should be observed with the mare's hind-quarters and her surroundings.

Sometimes the mare, from debility or other causes, foals while lying down, and unless she gets up immediately the foal is born, the navel-string is not torn, so that the young creature may remain attached to its parent through this medium unless some accident releases it, either the cord being ruptured or the membranes dragged from the uterus. If an attendant is at hand, however, the foal can be readily disengaged if he ties the cord firmly round with a piece of string in two places, about 6 or 8 inches from the foal, and cuts in through between the ties; this prevents bleeding from the mother and from the foal.

DIFFICULT PARTURITION

Though parturition is generally and apparently an easy and prompt act in the mare, yet it is not always so; on the contrary, in some instances it is extremely complicated and difficult, and many of these cases have a rapidly fatal termination. Hence the great need for careful observation of the mare at this time, for when the foal presents itself in the genital passage in an unfavorable position or abnormal attitude, unless the attendant has skills and experience it will fare badly with the mare, unless the assistance of a good veterinarian can be speedily procured. Unlike the cow, unless soon delivered, the mare quickly becomes greatly excited and restless, and even furious. All veterinarians who have had to deal with cases of difficult birth in mares are well aware of the herculean and dangerous task that often lies before them, when they are called upon to attend such cases, owing to the excitement, uneasiness, and only too frequently mad plunging animal, which is all the greater as parturition is protracted.

For this and other reasons it is imperative, if the foal is not born very soon after straining commences, that an examination should be made, and if the cause of obstruction cannot be discovered or speedily removed, then the veterinarian ought to be called with as little loss of time as possible, as every minute's delay increases the gravity of the case.

If the attendant possesses sufficient knowledge of veterinary obstetrics to enable him to deal with a comparatively simple case of difficult parturition when skilled assistance is not immediately available, then, or course, he will first make an examination in order to inform himself of the cause of obstruction to delivery. Should he find the foal in a favorable position, with the fore-legs presenting and the head forward or resting upon them with sufficient room for the young creature to pass through the canal, then prudence may induce him to wait a little, as the labor pains may not be strong enough to produce its expulsion. If, however, the position of the foal is not favorable to speedy birth it must be rectified, or if the labor pains are feeble, even when the position is good, and especially if some time has elapsed, then in both cases, steady and firm but not violent traction succeed in effecting delivery. It should be noted that some

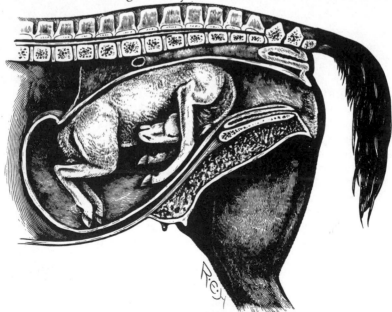

Neck presented, fore-legs directed backwards

old mares have a large pendulous abdomen, which is a hindrance to foaling, as the young creature is so much below the level of the passage through which it has to pass to reach the outer world, that the abdominal muscles--which are those chiefly concerned in the expulsion of the foal--cannot raise it high enough. In such a case it is most advantageous to elevate the abdomen by means of a sack passed beneath it, and lifted by strong men at each end.

When the foal itself is the cause of obstruction, this may be due to the position of the limbs, body, or head. The fore-limbs are perhaps most often at fault, and one or both are involved, the difficulty being generally caused by their being doubled back at the knees. A similar flexion of the hind-

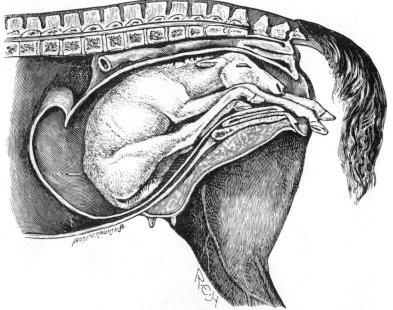

Head and all four legs presented

limbs at the hocks may occur and be a cause of difficult parturition. The head, instead of being placed nose forwards and between the fore-limbs, may be bent downwards towards the foal's chest or it and the neck may be thrown upwards and backwards, or towards the side of the foal's body.

Instead of the head and fore-limbs coming first, it may be the hind-limbs, or these may be retained and only the tail and buttocks presented while the body itself, instead of the back being towards the mare's back, may be reversed, the young creature lying more or less on its back with the legs upwards.

Besides all these and other malpositions or malpresentations here represented, there is the difficulty sometimes-though not very often in the cases of mares--occasioned by the presence of twins, as well as the occurrence of monstrosities, and serious deformities or morbid conditions in the foal. Deformity or diseases in the mare causing narrowing of the genital passage may also be a cause of hindrance to birth.

In cases of difficult parturition in the mare, much skill, adroitness, patience, and resource, as well as physical strength and agility, are required in dealing with the very numerous and diverse obstacles that have to be encountered and overcome if the lives of the foal and mother, or either, are to be saved. More especially are judgment and manual tact re-

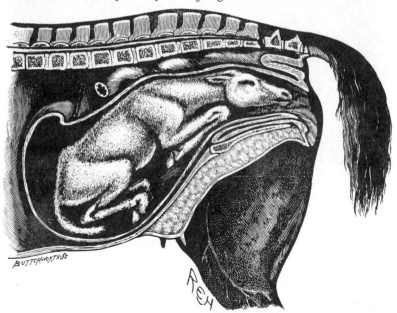

Head presented, knees doubled back

quired in making an examination. This demands not only a thorough knowledge of the internal anatomy of the mare's reproductive organs, healthy and pathological, but also an acquaintance by touch with all the surface and different regions of the foal's body and limbs. Without this knowledge and tactile facility it may be impossible to understand the hindrance to birth, and to render assistance by adopting proper measures or resorting to effective manuvers. So that the amateur or unskilled operator is likely to do more harm than good, and may even unawares convert what to an expert would prove a comparatively simple case, into a most difficult if not altogether hopeless one.

MALPRESENTATIONS

Head Presented, Knees Doubled Back

To effect delivery while the foal is in this abnormal condition is practically impossible. What is required is to bring the legs into the position of a natural presentation, i.e. into the passage, with the head resting upon them. To effect this the canon bone must be straightened on the knee and the leg extended. The limb most easy of access is the first to be dealt with. If the head is in the passage it must be forced back into the uterus by planting the flat of the hand on the front of the face. When necessary, this may be effected with a crutch made to press on the front of the chest. While this is being done by an assistant, the operator will pass his hand along the under side of the neck until the forearm is reached. A push in a backward direction should then be made, until the arm can be raised and the leg brought bodily forward. The hand should now pass down to the canon, seize it, and through it push the knee up towards the neck. The hand while drawing the limb forward gradually moves towards the pastern, which it firmly grips, and after extending the fetlock-joint, draws the foot into the passage. The limb having been secured by cords, the recovery of the next one may be proceeded with, after which delivery will be effected in the usual way.

Still more difficult is that presentation where one fore-limb with the head is in the passage, and the other is lying far back under the body. Here the advantage of a long arm and a strong man to use it will be clearly obvious, for, as in the last presentation, the success of the operation will depend upon the displaced fore-limb being secured and brought into position. The passage must first be cleared by pushing back the head. The hand should then be passed along the under part of the neck, should seize the fore-arm and bring it forward into the passage.

If this cannot be accomplished, then the front parts of the dam must be raised by underpacking the fore-feet with litter so as to give the body an inclination backward. When the forearm is reached the hand should follow it downward to the knee, or as near it as possible. The limb is then firmly grasped and drawn forwards.

When the arm has been brought in a straight line with the pelvic inlet, it should then be used to push the body back into the uterus with a crutch implanted against the breast.

If it should happen that the arm cannot be reached, an attempt must be made to pass a cord round it. The leg will

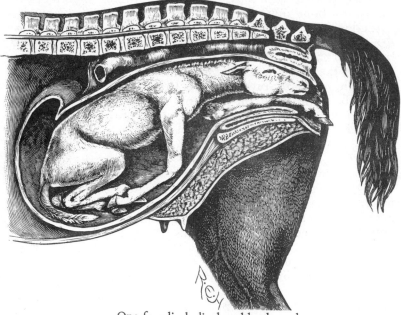

One fore-limb displaced backwards

then be pulled forwards by assistants, while the operator, seizing the canon and then the pastern, will engage himself in directing it into the passage.

Posterior or Breech Presentation

The breech of the fetus may be presented either with the hind-legs in the passage or projected forward under the abdomen. In the former position delivery may be effected without assistance, but it is always desirable to afford help promptly where the least difficulty arises. This position is the most favorable breech form of presentation, since it requires no readjustment of parts. All that is necessary is to supplement the natural force of the throes with manual assistance from without.

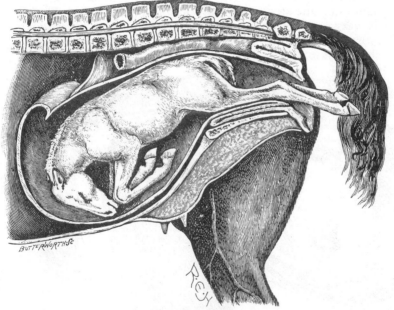

Breech presentation, hind-legs in passage

It is otherwise where the hocks are flexed and presented with the breech, and the legs extended forward under the belly. In this presentation there is danger of the parts being wedged in the pelvis, and so fixed as to render a proper ad-

justment difficult if not impossible. Before delivery can be
effected in this case the direction of the hind-limbs must be
changed and they must be brought into the passage. To
effect this it is necessary that room be provided by forcing
the buttocks in a forward direction so as to clear a space for
bringing up the hind-limbs. In performing this task, advantage will be obtained if the hind extremities of the mare be
raised by underpacking with litter or some other suitable
means. A forward and downward inclination will thus be
given to the fetus, and the resistance to pressure from behind
thereby reduced. When this has been done, an attempt
should be made to force the body of the foal forward, either
by means of the hand or a crutch applied to the buttocks
immediately below the tail. In this connection it is necessary
to point out that the force employed should not be sudden
and spasmodic, but steady, continuous, and progressive. The
intervals between the throes are periods when the fetus will
yield most to pressure, and the advantage gained at these
times should not be lost, if possible, when straining returns.

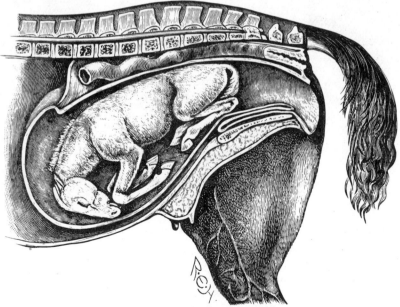

Breech and hocks presented

Room having been thus provided, an attempt should now be made to bring the hind-legs into position for delivery. For this purpose the palm of the hand should be placed against the under side of the point of the hock, and pressure made in a forward and slightly upward direction upon the second thigh. If by a little manuvering a cord can be placed round the bend of the hock, it should be done and handed to an assistant, who will be able to render considerable help by pulling the limb backwards when the right time comes.

The operator should now grasp the shin-bone, and with such help as his assistant can give him, draw the leg towards the pelvic inlet. As soon as the pastern or the foot can be reached, the fetlock-joint should be forcibly flexed and the leg lifted into the passage. Before this can be done it may be necessary to pass a cord round the pastern and bring traction to bear upon it, while the operator presses the point of the hock in an upward and forward direction. After one-limb has been adjusted/the other must be dealt with in the same manner.

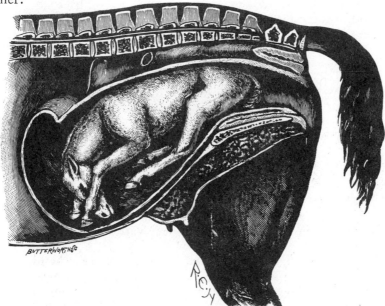

Breech presentation, legs extended beneath abdomen

A still more troublesome and dangerous breech presentation is that where the hind-legs, instead of being flexed as in
the case referred to above, are carried forward and downward
towards the fore-limbs, and the thigh bent upon the pelvis
allows the croup and buttocks to be presented.

Unless this misplacement is promptly recognized and
corrected, the difficulty will be aggravated by the straining,
which, while forcing the breech backward into the pelvis,
causes the hind-limbs to be moved farther forward at the
same time, thus adding to the already serious difficulty of the
case. Here "the rational indication is, or course, to extend
the limbs of the fetus backwards, as in ordinary breech presentation, and to give these and the body a direction in har-
mony with the axis and dimensions of the pelvic inlet, so
that birth may be effected by the combined efforts of the
mother and the obstetrist". But this indication is often most
difficult to fulfil, though in some instances it is possible when
labor is not too advanced, and when the fetus, still in the
abdominal cavity, is movable, and can be pushed sufficiently
from the inlet to allow the lower part of the limbs to be
seized and brought into the vagina.

Pushing the fetus as far into the abdomen as possible, one
of the limbs is seized above the hock, and the thigh flexed
as completely as circumstances will permit, by lifting that
joint towards the mother's sacrum. Still pushing the fetus
off by means of the repeller or crutch, the hand is passed
down to the hoof until the toe is reached and enclosed in the
palm; by adopting this precaution danger of injury to the
uterus or vagina is averted. Then the foot is brought into the
passage by flexing all the joints on each other. Again, pushing the fetus forward, the same manuver is repeated with the
other limb, if necessary, and delivery is proceeded with.

Neck Presented, Two Fore-Limbs In The Passage

The difficulty in bringing about a natural presentation in
this case will be in proportion to the backward displacement
of the head.

Should this be slight, it may only require that the hand
be passed under the chin or into the mouth, and the head
raised into the passage. Where, however, the neck is much
bent, and the head carried under the brisket with the poll

firmly fixed against the pelvic brim, considerable difficulty will be experienced in restoring the parts to their proper position.

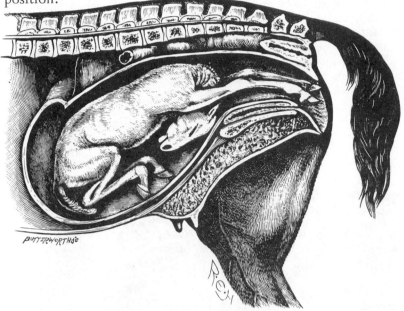

Neck presented, fore-limbs in passage

The first requirement will be to push the body backwards by means of a powerful arm, or failing in this, crutches applied to the front of the shoulders. By doing this, room will be provided for the forward movement of the head. An attempt must now be made to raise the latter by seizing such parts as come within reach to which traction may be applied. The ears will be first accessible, or blunt hooks may be inserted into the orbits, or passed behind the lower jaw or into the angle of the mouth. It is necessary to point out that in order to obtain the full benefit of the measures suggested above, the backward force should be applied to the body at the same time as the forward pull if made upon the head.

Breast Presented, Legs In The Passage

The head may also be displaced laterally, i.e., thrown back on to the right or left side of the neck or body. Here again

the degree of displacement will vary in different cases. Sometimes the head is merely flexed on the neck, while in others
the neck is bent backward and may carry the head as far as
the flank. The long neck of the foal tends to render these
presentations difficult and sometimes impossible to rectify
The most successful plan of action is as follows: Cord the
presenting fore-feet, push the fetus into the uterus so as to
clear it from the pelvic inlet, pushing either on the flexed
neck or chest, and not directly backward, but rather oblique-
ly to the side opposite that to which the head inclines, so as
to bring this round to the inlet. If the fore-limbs are in the
way of the operator they may also be pushed back into the
uterus. The head should then be sought for and brought into
position.

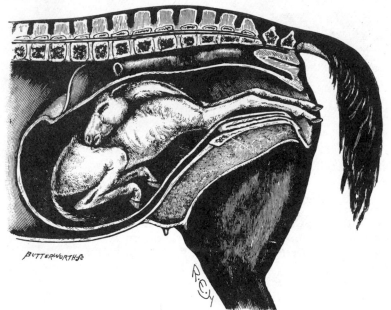

Legs and breast presented

Here the ears are the most accessible parts to which force
may be applied; then, if necessary, blunt hooks may be inserted into the orbits, or into the angles of the mouth, and
the head drawn forwards by means of cords, while the body

is being pushed backwards with a crutch or repeller. When the head has been brought into line with the body, delivery is then effected in the usual way. Besides this faulty position the head may also be thrown upwards and backwards while the fore-limbs are presented in the passage. As we have already pointed out, these are always most difficult tasks, and require a large practical experience, skill and judgment to ensure success. They are not such as to be undertaken by the amateur if professional assistance can be procured.

MECHANICAL AIDS TO DELIVERY

Mechanical aids in difficult operations become indispensable to success, and it is of the first importance that whoever undertakes their use should clearly understand the particular purpose for which they are designed, as also their mode of adjustment. These qualifications cannot be imparted by any written description, but must be acquired by experience and practice.

In proceeding to deliver a mare, the uterus should first be freely explored until the precise position of the fetus has been determined; then the steps necessary to bring it into a natural presentation and effect its removal should be carefully considered.

In this connection it should always be in the mind of the operator that where two feet are presented they may not belong to the same animal, and before delivery is attempted he should fully satisfy himself that he is not dealing with twins, from each of which a foot may proceed.

Where but one foal exists, it is equally important to be assured that the feet in the passage are both fore-feet, and not one of each. The application of force while these precautions are neglected would endanger the life of both dam and offspring.

It may be found that the existing malposition is such as can be rectified by a little judicious employment of the hands alone, or that the use of ropes, repellers, hooks, or pulleys, or all these several appliances, will be called for in the course of delivery. Besides the mechanical aids, it must not be overlooked that the mare may be made to lend herself to the process of delivery by being placed in certain special positions. By raising the hind-quarters with litter, the fetus may be thrown forward and more room afforded the operator in rectifying the presentation, or it may be desirable to place her in the reverse position by underpacking in front.

It is a good working rule to secure with ropes or other means all parts which are found to be in the passage whatever they may be, and to keep them under control until it has been fully decided that they are not necessary to delivery.

Many parts of the body of the fetus are available for the application of ropes and other instruments, by and through which to bring traction to bear upon the fetus.

A stop-noose may be applied round the neck, a light head-stall extemporized out of a strong cord may be fitted to the head. A running noose passed into the mouth and carried over the poll, or applied round the lower jaw, will aid materially in the application of force, and the same may be said of ropes applied above the hock or knee, or the fetlock, or the foot.

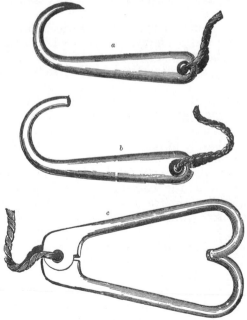

Hooks or crotchets a. sharp   b.blunt   c.double

When no sufficient hold can be secured by these means, hooks of various descriptions may be brought into use; but it must be understood that, while in trained hands they are most useful auxiliaries, in the hands of the unskilled they may prove dangerous and even deadly instruments. Hooks or crotchets may be sharp or blunt, single or double. Some are attached to ropes, and others are fixed to handles. The crutch or repeller is another means of moving the body of the foal backwards into the womb when it is desired to make room for securing and changing the position of one or more of the extremities. Blunt hooks connected with a rod will be found useful to anchor on to the angle of the mouth or the orbit of the eye, when these parts are placed beyond the reach of the hand, and in critical cases, when the mare is in danger and a firm hold is imperative, sharp ones may also be made available in connection with the latter. In applying them, however, care should be taken to implant them well into the orbit, and to avoid the use of excessive force, lest we should tear out and injure the walls of the uterus.

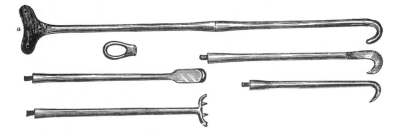

Gowing's parturition instrument a.crutch or repeller

When no sufficient hold can be secured by any other means, double hooks or crotchet forceps, blunt or pointed, may be employed.

Double crotchets will be found serviceable in a variety of conditions, and especially when no sufficient hold can be secured by other means. These instruments may be made to enter the tissues and take a firm hold of deep-seated tendons or ligaments, or be anchored on to bones.

In employing these several aids to delivery it should be understood that everything which it may be found necessary

Pollock's obstetric forceps, with double hooks

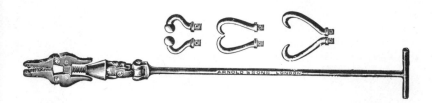

to introduce into the uterus or genital passage should be thoroughly clean and disinfected, and the same precaution also applies to the hands of the operator, whose nails should be cut short as a safeguard against injury to the womb.

When force is employed in the removal of the fetus it should be steady, regular, and continuous. Jerky and spasmodic traction avails but little, and may be actually injurious both to dam and offspring. The effort, when commenced should be sustained, and increased steadily with each labor pain, so that the outward force and the inward force shall continue and operate simultaneously. Until the head has passed through the vulva the pull should be directly backwards, then slightly inclined downwards so as to prevent the withers jamming against the upper boundary of the pelvic outlet. As the shoulders pass through the pelvic outlet the resistance will be very considerably increased. To overcome it a pull should be taken slightly to one side and then to the other, and the same alternation of movement may be practised when the hips drag in the passage.

Where the case is protracted and signs of exhaustion appear in the mare, the efforts must be sustained by the administration of stimulants and a short rest. The necessity for this may be frequently avoided where plenty of force is provided early, while the mare is fresh and full of energy. Many mares are annually sacrificed from neglect of this precaution, and veterinarians rightly complain that delivery is frequently rendered impossible, and the life of the mare jeopardized by the "pulling about" she suffers, for want of sufficient well-directed force at the outset.

CARE OF MARE AND FOAL AFTER PARTURITION

After parturition, and if mare and foal are getting on well, warmth, comfort, cleanliness, and a plentiful supply of good food are all that are necessary while they are under cover. The most favorable, and therefore the most natural, time for mares to foal is during the months of March, April, and May, when the weather is, or should be, propitious and grass is plentiful. At this period, if the mare has been pastured before foaling, she and the foal may soon be allowed out of the loose-box to the paddock if the weather be fine, as nothing can be more invigorating for both than a run at grass, if only for an hour or two at first, though they must on no account be exposed to rain or cold winds if such exposure can possibly be avoided.

In the loose-box, good hay and a small allowance of crushed oats two or three times a day should be given; and if grass is not available, and especially if the mare does not furnish a sufficient supply of milk, grain supplements may be allowed frequently, and with great advantage. Crushed oats is especially to be recommended for the mare when the foal is a few weeks old, as the foal begins to nibble at and soon to eat them, and thus to prepare itself in the best way for being weaned, while this addition to its food will greatly tend to its robustness and development.

The foal itself is not liable to many diseases if properly cared for. At birth the attendant should give it his immediate attention if it does not immediately breathe, as unless he then acts promptly it may die. When it fails to inspire after the navel-string has been divided, he should at once open its mouth, seize the tongue, and pull it gently forwards a few times at some seconds interval blowing hard into the mouth and nostrils while the tongue is forward. Flicking the sides of the chest with a wet towel at intervals may also produce the desired effect.

VII. GROWTH OF THE FOAL

In but a few centuries the large, highly-nervous race-horse, with his wonderful speed and courage, has been evolved out of Eastern and European ponies. Some breeders are now engaged in breeding pigmy horses little over 30 inches in height, others are as successfully breeding huge, powerful animals as wonderful in their way as their pigmy relatives. It may even be said that a recognized part of the breeder's work consists in modifying, through changes in the external conditions, the animals to which he happens to devote his special attention, just as horticulturists, by food, heat, and timely shelter, alter plants until all resemblance to their wild stock is as good as lost.

Breeders of Shetland and polo ponies, and, for that matter, breeders of Thoroughbred and Quarter Horses know well enough that to have any chance of success they must exercise the utmost vigilance over the conditions under which their foals, colts, and fillies are reared. A major consideration as to these conditions is the feed supplied. Often the breeder is unaware when changes in the food, temperature, etc. are likely to produce the desired effect.

In studying the rate of growth of the horse, on the one hand allowance must be made for the influence of the external conditions, and on the other for hereditary influences, i.e. the stereotyped changes ultimately due to the environment.

The difference between a tall and an undersized man is mainly a difference in the length of the legs; but in the case of the horse the height, as commonly understood, instead of bearing, as in man, an intimate relation with the length of the hind-limbs, is intimately related to the length of the fore-limbs.

101

The height of a horse, it is hardly necessary to state, depends mainly on (1) the length from the elbow to the ground; (2) the length and obliquity of the arm-bone (*humerus*); and (3) the length of certain spines of the dorsal vertebrae, the spines which give rise to the more or less arched ridge known as the withers.

In the living animal it is impossible to measure the length of the vertebral spines, and only possible to estimate roughly the length and obliquity of the humerus, and hence it will be necessary in studying the rate of growth in the horse to trust chiefly to the length of the fore-limb as measured from the elbow to the ground. In man the limbs belong to the common or ordinary vertebrate type, but in the horse they have departed as far from the general plan as highly useful structures well could, for instead of five digits, as in man, there is but one complete digit, and in their hard parts the limbs are infinitely more highly specialized than is the case in any other mammal, and more profoundly altered than even the wing of a bat.

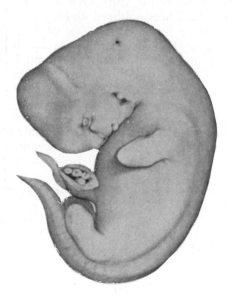

Horse embryo (five weeks)

In the case of the horse, the first rudiments of limbs appear in the form of short bud-like outgrowths between the twenty-first and twenty-eighth days. The growth is at the outset so deliberate that even at the end of the fifth week the limb rudiments are only 2 mm. (about 1/8 inch) in length. After a time, however, the rate of growth is accelerated, with the result that before the middle of gestation (the twenty-fourth week) is reached they are relatively as large as in the full-grown horse. Havings reached this size, it might be assumed that they would continue to maintain the same proportions up to the time of birth. This assumption would, however, be wide of the mark, and in fact would never be made by anyone aware of the great relative length of the legs in the new-born foal. To have a chance of surviving in a wild state-of escaping prowling wolves or hungry jackals, and hunting dogs--a foal must almost from the moment of its appearance on the scene be capable of keeping up with the herd into which it is so unceremoniously introduced--sometimes apparently to the annoyance of the ever-watchful leader and head of the family. To succeed in this it requires legs long enough to gallop at least as fast as the older members of the herd. It is doubtless for this reason that during the second half of the period of gestation the limbs grow very much faster than the trunk, with the result that for some weeks before birth they are relatively not only extremely long, but so wonderfully perfect in all their parts that, as in certain other wild ungulates, a foal is no sooner ushered into the world than it is galloping merrily along, carefully shadowed by its dam.

A small horse embryo of about 7 mm. in length, a twenty or at the most twenty-one days embryo, is somewhat fish-like in form, but quite limbless. Soon after the end of the third week limbs appear in the form of minute buds. At the end of the fourth week they are easily recognized, and by the end of the fifth week they are 2 mm. in length, and is not unlike a human embryo of the same age; by the end of the fifth week it is 5-6 mm. longer. At first the limb buds are simple paddle-like, structureless outgrowths, but during the fifth week rudiments of the skeleton appear; while during the sixth week they are so rotated and flexed that the position of the elbow and wrist (commonly called the "knee") can be made out in the fore-limb, and in both fore-and hind

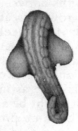

Hind limbs and tail (four weeks)

Hind limbs and tail (six weeks)

limb there are indications of three digits (2-4). Even at the end of the sixth week, when the embryo is 2 cm. in length, the fore-limbs only measure 4 mm., and the hind-limbs are but little longer. Marked progress is made during the seventh week, with the result that before the eighth week is reached the limbs have all the distinctive equine characters and are about one-third of the total length of the embryo--the embryo measuring 3 cm., the limbs nearly 1 cm. Before the eighth week is reached not only are the elbow and "knee" evident, but the fetlock and frog of both fore-and hind-limbs are fairly well moulded, and in the latter the true knee (stifle) and hock are well defined, the distance from the hock to the tip of the developing hoof being 7 mm. By the end of the eighth week we have a horse in miniature. At this stage (the total length of the embryo being 6.5 cm.) the distance from the withers to the tip of the curved and pointed hoof is 3.3 cm., from the elbow 1.9 cm., while the length from the hock is 1.3 cm.

During the eighth week the embryo nearly doubles its length , but during the three following weeks there is an increase in bulk rather than in length.   At the end of the eleventh week the total length is 10.2 cm., the length from the elbow being 3.15 cm. from the withers 5.2 cm., and from the hock 2.4.

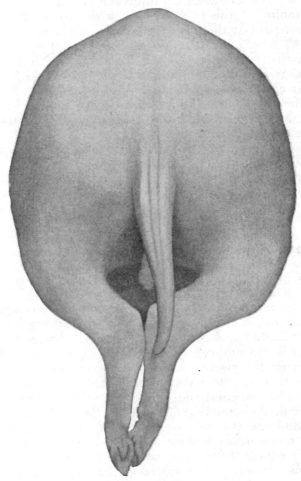

Hind limbs and tail (eight weeks)

From the eleventh to the fifteenth week the embryo again more than doubles its length, and increases considerably in weight. At the end of the fifteenth week the length is 23 cm., the height at withers 14 cm., the length from the elbow 8.8 cm., and from the hock 6.6 cm. Again, from the fifteenth to the twenty-fourth week the total length is nearly doubled, while the length of the limbs is more than doubled. At the beginning of the twentieth week the total length is 28 cm., the height at the withers 19.5 cm., the length from the elbow 12.3 cm., and from the hock 9.2 cm. By the time the twenty-fifth week is reached the total length of the young horse is 43.5 cm., the height at the withers 32.5 cm., the length from the elbow 21 cm., and from the hock 15 cm., the circumference below the knee being 3 cm. As already mentioned, before the middle of gestation is approached--i.e. prior to the twenty-fourth week--the bones of the limbs are as nearly as possible of the same relative length as in the adult.

This fact is best brought out by comparing the limb bones of a five-and-a-half months embryo with the corresponding structures in the adult. In the thoroughbred horse Hermit the humerus measured 33.5 cm., the radius 37.5 cm., and the third metacarpal 25.5 cm. In a twenty-three-weeks embryo the humerus is 6.5 cm. in length, and the radius 7.3 cm.--i.e. the radius bears exactly the same relation to the humerus as in the case of Hermit. Again, the middle (III) metacarpal in a half-time embryo, to agree with the corresponding bone in Hermit, should measure 5.0 cm.; its actual length is 5.5 cm., i.e. it is already 5 mm. relatively longer than in Hermit; but this is more than counterbalanced in the twenty-three-weeks embryo by the phalanges being relatively shorter. From the twenty-fourth week onwards the limbs grow faster than the trunk. In the front the increase in growth is mainly beyond the wrist-joint, while in the hind-limbs it is chiefly beyond the knee-joint or stifle. In both fore-and hind-limbs the increase is greatest for some time in the middle metacarpals and metatarsals--i.e. in the fore and hind cannon bones. In the case of Hermit (the 1867 Derby winner whose skeleton is preserved in the Royal Veterinary College Museum, London, England), when the humerus is taken as equal to 100, the third metacarpal is equal to 76.1.

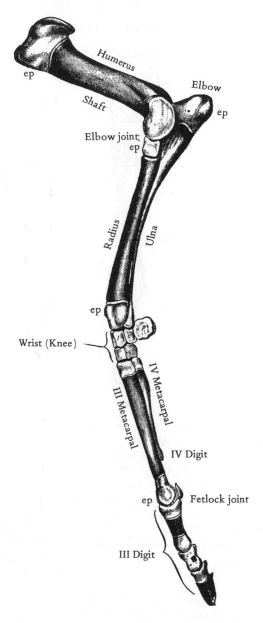

Fore-limb (twenty-three weeks), front view

Fore-limb (twenty-three weeks)

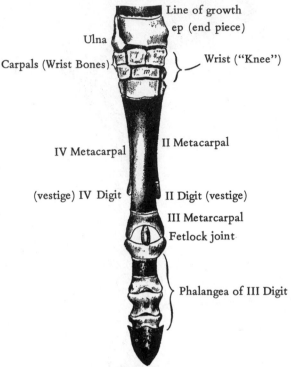

Line of growth

ep (end piece)

Ulna

Carpals (Wrist Bones)

Wrist ("Knee")

IV Metacarpal

II Metacarpal

(vestige) IV Digit

II Digit (vestige)

III Metarcarpal

Fetlock joint

Phalangea of III Digit

In a seven-months fetus however, with the humerus equal to 100, the third metacarpal may be over 90, while at nine months it may be over 110, and at birth 130--i.e. relatively well-nigh twice the length of the third metacarpal in Hermit. A similar rate of growth characterizes the third metatarsal bone. This increase in the cannon bones during the second half of the period of gestation explains to a large extent the great length of the foal's legs at birth; it also accounts for the fact that the cannon bones--the bones considered of so immense importance in all kinds of horses--increase but little in length after birth. In the case of a thoroughbred, e.g., the third metacarpal appears only to increase 3 cm. (barely 1¼ inch) after birth, while the main bone of the fore-arm (the *radius*) often increases 9 cm. (3½ inches), or nearly three times as much as the front cannon bone. Though the cannon bones may only increase 1 inch in length after birth, they may increase 3 or even 4 inches in circumference in a 14-hand horse.

From the twenty-fourth to the beginning of the thirty-fourth week, horse embryos often increase at the withers from 32.5 cm. to 54 cm., while from the elbow onwards the increase is from 21 cm. to 34.5 cm., and from the point of the hock to the tip of the hoof the increase is 10.5 cm.--i.e. from 15 cm. to 25.5 cm.

At the fortieth week the embryo is about 86 cm. in length, the height at the withers being 76 cm.; from the elbow to the point of the hoof the distance is 52-53 cm., and from the hock 40-42 cm.

Of the 22 cm. of increase in height from the thirty-fourth to the beginning of the fortieth week, 19 cm. is due to the lengthening of the leg from the elbow downwards; but during the last eight weeks (i.e. 40-48) of fetal life there is only an increase of about 9 cm. from the elbow to the ground, while the total increase at the withers is over 20 cm.

At birth the foal of 14-hand parents may be expected to measure 92 cm. at the withers, 62 cm. from the point of the elbow, and 45 cm. from the point of the hock to the ground, the circumference below the knee being 10 cm.

From these figures it appears that during development the actual increase in the length of the limbs is greatest between the twenty-fourth and fortieth weeks. The rate of growth at the withers and from the elbow and hock downwards during development is graphically represented in the accompanying chart. Further enquiries may show that during the last eight weeks of fetal life there is a rapid formation of bone, a hardening of tendons and ligaments, and a strengthening of the muscles so that immediately after birth the foal may, even in times of stress, keep its place in the herd.

The rate of growth of the foal is decidedly unequal even during the first three months. It might have been assumed either that the increase would be continuous and equal during the first two or three years, or that, rapid at first, it would gradually diminish as the growth power of the bones was lost. It appears however, that the growth, rapid during

TABLE I. — SHOWING RATE OF GROWTH OF A 14-HANDS HORSE
DURING DEVELOPMENT

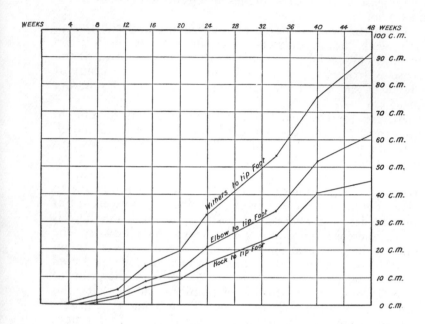

the first month, is inconsiderable during the second, but more pronounced during the third, while from the fifth month onwards the rate of growth may be said to diminish gradually, there being, however, ups and downs related to the shedding of the coat, weaning, or other distrubing causes.

During the first month the growth at the withers is 11.4 cm., during the second 3 cm., and during the third 10 cm. Throughout the second three months (4 to 6 inclusive) the growth at the withers is about the same as during the third month; from the seventh to the ninth month it is 6 cm., from the tenth to the twelfth 5 cm. Hence, during the first year the total increase in height at the withers may be all but 42 cm. (16½ inches). During the entire second year the growth may not exceed 8 cm. (3¼ inches), and during the third year it may amount to less than an inch. After the third year increase in height, if there is any, results almost entirely from a further lengthening of the verebral spines that form the skeleton of the withers--the length of these spines is intimately related to the size and weight of the head.

Of the increase of height during the first six months 17.7 cm. are due to the growth of the fore-limb from the point of the elbow downwards, but during the second six months the increase of the fore-arm, wrist, and foot is only 3.7 cm., and after the first year the fore-limb from the el-bow downwards only increases 1.4 cm. It is worthy of note that almost the entire increase in the length of the fore-limb below the elbow is due to the growth of the radius. The cir-cumference below the knee increases considerably during the first year. In the case of the hind-limb there is a gradual in-crease from the point of the hock during the first nine months, when the maximum length is often reached--the in-crease is mainly due to a lengthening of the phalanges and the heel process of the os calcis, not to the middle met-atarsal.

TABLE II. — SHOWING THE RATE OF GROWTH OF A 14-HANDS
HORSE DURING THE FIRST YEAR

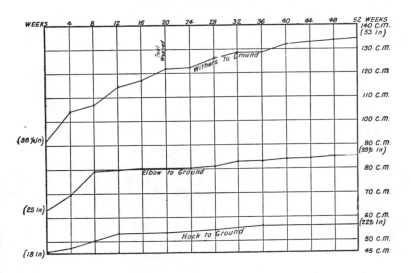

TABLE III. – SHOWING RATE OF GROWTH IN A HORSE DURING THE FIRST THREE YEARS

Age.	Height at Withers.	Height at Croup.	Girth.	Length from top of Head to line between upper margin of Nostrils.	Length from inner corner of Eye to upper margin of Nostril.	Length from point of Elbow to ground, the Leg occupying a vertical position.	Length from point of Hock to ground, the Shank having a vertical position.	Circumference below Knee.
	In.	In.	In.	In.	In.	In.	In.	In.
At birth	36½	38	30	12¼	5½	25	18	4¼
End of 1 month ...	41	42½	38½	14	6¼	27½	19	4¾
,, 2 ,, ...	42⅛	44⅛	42	15¼	7	30⅛	20⅛	5¼
,, 3 ,, ...	45⅛	46¾	46	15⅞	7¼	30¼	21¼	5¾
,, 4 ,, ...	46¾	48¾	48	17⅛	7½	31⅝	21¼	5¾
,, 5 ,, ...	48	49	49½	17⅛	8	31⅝	21¼	5¾
,, 6 ,, ...	48⅛	49⅜	52	17½	8¼	31¾	21½	6
,, 7 ,, ...	49¾	51¼	53½	17¾	8⅜	32	21¾	6
,, 8 ,, ...	50½	52	54	18	8½	32¾	22⅛	6
,, 9 ,, ...	50⅝	53¼	56	18¼	9	33	22½	6
,, 10 ,, ...	51⅞	53⅜	56½	18½	9⅛	33	22½	6
,, 11 ,, ...	52½	53¾	57¼	19	9½	33¼	22½	6⅛
,, 12 ,, ...	53	54	59	19½	9¾	33½	22½	6¼
,, 24 ,, ...	56¼	56½	64	20¼	10¼	33¾	22½	6¾
,, 36 ,, ...	57	58	68	20½	10½	33¾	22½	7½

The length of the head gradually increases all through the first year, when the maximum length is nearly attained. The increase is mainly below the orbit, the space between the inner canthus of the eye and the upper margin of the nostril being nearly doubled during the first two years.

It will be noticed from the accompanying chart that the girth is all but doubled during the first year.

Why, it may be asked, is the growth in the horse arrested so much sooner than in man? In the horse, as in man, the majority of the long bones consist of a shaft and of two end-pieces (*epiphyses*). The increase in the length of the typical long bones takes place at the junction of the shaft with the epiphyses. This zone of growth is a source of weakness, and the sooner the terminal pieces--which by their free ends enter into the joints--firmly coalesce with the shaft the better. In the horse this fusion takes place at a comparatively early stage, and when it has been once effected all further increase in length become impossible.

The question may now be asked: Can any practical use be made of all this information as to the rate of growth in the horse? It is often taken for granted that the sire counts for infinitely more than the dam. If the sire happens to be more impressive then the dam, he will doubtless count for most in the characteristics of the offspring; but a sire, however good, can no more make up for want of quality in the dam than good seed can yield a good return regardless of the nature of the soil in which it is sown. To begin with, it is quite important that the germ cell provided by the dam should be as perfect in every respect as the infinitely smaller sperm cell supplied by the sire. Further, unless before development begins there is stored up an abundant supply of the material needed for the developing embryo, and unless all through the period of gestation the food contains the ingredients requisite for building up the bones and other tissues of the developing foal, the result must of necessity prove disappointing. However perfect the sire, he can no more assist in providing nourishment or suitable conditions during development than he can assist in ministering to the want of the foal after birth.

But the enquiry as to the rate of growth of the foal mainly shows that from the sixth week of development there is an ever-increasing demand for bone-forming material. This demand , great enough during the later months of gestation, is especially urgent during the first three months after birth perhaps during the first five months for it is during this period that the growth of the bones mainly takes place. It may hence be said that, with the help of the information given here, the breeder should be better able so to regulate the food of his brood mares that an abundant supply of bone-forming material will be available not only during, but for some months after, gestation, and will be in a position so to treat his colts during their first two years that they may reach either a maximum, an average, or a small size, and whatever the size, will be provided with the best possible chance of forming large ivory-like bones, and, what is perhaps of equal importance, strong ligaments and tendons capable of withstanding sudden jars and strains.